JANE DOE #9

HOW I SURVIVED
R. KELLY

LIZZETTE MARTINEZ
KEELIN MacGREGOR

WILDBLUE
PRESS

WildBluePress.com

JANE DOE #9 published by:
WILDBLUE PRESS
P.O. Box 102440
Denver, Colorado 80250

WILDBLUE PRESS is registered at the U.S. Patent and Trademark Offices.

ISBN 978-1-952225-86-4 Trade Paperback
ISBN 978-1-952225-85-7 eBook

Cover design © 2021 WildBlue Press. All rights reserved.

Interior Formatting/Cover Design by Elijah Toten
www.totencreative.com

JANE DOE #9

This is dedicated to my beautiful mother Rosa Maria Santiago and grandmothers, Delia Olmeda Roldan & Felecita Ortega Santiago, the ultimate survivors who taught me how to be a warrior woman. Your strength runs through my blood and I thank you for it!

Te amo!

Lissie

INTRO

I'm waiting. Waiting every day on pins and needles—watching the news, looking up articles, updating the same sites in my laptop browser over and over, and contacting my lawyer in hopes she has insight unavailable to the general public. Waiting for justice.

I didn't know for sure if I would be listed in the indictment as a potential witness. They asked me to be a witness—the FBI did—but you never know. Still, I stand with all the survivors, whether we're put on the stand or not. Whether we've been able to publicly come out or not. Every time I see these ladies on the stand, I pray. Hard. The day Jerhonda took the stand, I bit off all my nails and pulled out some of my hair. I was so nervous for her. I'm watching my sisters as they're labeled "groupies" or "super fans" for testifying about things that happened years ago. Still? Even now, in new relationships, with new lives, trying to move on from their pain, there are people still trying to dumb it down into something so ridiculously simple?

The bullying has only gotten worse, and depression in this waiting period hit me so hard I couldn't get out of bed. I hear holes in certain accounts; stories I've heard firsthand. Stories protecting him. I want to throw up.

Nothing I do right now leads to anything more than waiting. I'm on the list, but who knows if I'll go testify. In the meantime, I can't sleep. My anxiety, depression, and insomnia keep getting worse. I feel exhausted, emotionally drained, and physically depleted. Sounds like the last twenty years or so repeating itself.

I'm ready to get on that stand if I need to, though, because there should never be the opportunity for another woman to be hurt by this man. Robert Kelly.

I am Jane Doe #9.

PROLOGUE

"*Where is Robert?*"

"C'mon, Lizzette, you know he could be anywhere. Probably at the studio. Oblivious to the world."

When none of my calls to Robert went through, I had dialed Demetrius again. To my surprise, he finally answered, but he's not giving me anything.

"Where is he?" I repeat.

"I don't know, Hon. He's not answering the phone for me either."

"Bullshit. Where are you?"

"Lizzette, I already said, I don't know where he is!"

I hate you. Both of you.

It's taking every ounce of effort to not smash the phone against the wall. I've become one more scattered piece of Rob's life to be put away in a box of a hotel room for safekeeping while he does whatever he wants without consequences.

The food I ordered to the room earlier is sitting on the floor congealing and hardening in the open air. I had only managed a few bites before the nausea and pain kicked in, forcing me to stop and set the fork aside for good. These cramps just keep getting worse. As a more insistent pang bites into my abdomen, I curl up around the phone on the floor.

"Demetrius, I'm coming to you," I mutter through clenched teeth.

"What? He's not with me. He's in his own *thing* right now, dealing with stuff his way. Please, Lizzette, you got to understand."

"I have to understand what?" I shout, throwing the Nokia cell phone across the room. It's Rob's anyway. He paid for it, continues to pay for it, and uses it to check up on everything I do and who I talk to. *Well, now's your chance to check up on me. Any minute now would be fantastic.* I roll to my knees, push up off the floor with trembling arms, and stagger to the large windows facing out toward the Chicago city streets.

Staring out the thick glass windowpane of the hotel, I imagine what it would be like to fall through, to step into the air away from heartache, disappear from all this trouble. Would my soul drift up into the sky so I could look down one more time on the lights reflecting off Lake Michigan?

What about your unborn baby?

Hot tears crowd my eyes as I press my hands against the chilled glass, almost wishing it would give in and let me go. I start pacing around the small suite to distract my mind. There's plenty of room to move around. Rob can afford all this, provide all this, but he's not here now, when it's so important.

Warmth spreads along my leg and I glance down at jeans blotched wet and dark. *Shit. Where is he?* Dropping to the floor, I'm hunting for the previously thrown Nokia when the room phone interrupts my search. Scrambling, I pull it down beside me as the cramps double me over again. Knees buckled under, my forehead rests against soft carpet.

"Rob?!"

"Hello, this is the front desk calling. We have a message for R. Kelly."

"Wait, he's not even here. You don't mean a message *from* R. Kelly?"

"No, sorr—"

Second flying phone of the night. Christ. I call my best friend Michella on the block of a cell phone I finally located. Peeling off the damp pants, I drag myself to the shower to rinse off the blood. Red swirls down the drain in a sickening spiral.

"Go back to the hospital!" Michella's voice is frantic and loud in my ear. "Now! Lizzette, you have to listen to me."

"He's not here… can't take me…" My head is heavy. Hard to hold up. "Nobody is here. Not allowed to leave on my own. Is… is against the rules." My best friend is cursing up a storm, but it's a distant drone. Everything is running together. Words and surroundings drip over each other like fresh paint in the rain. I can't pick anything apart. No idea what she's saying. Can't remember what I was doing.

Another spike of pain pulls my knees tight to my chest, phone forgotten on the cold tiles. How many days has he been gone? I can't remember. The doctor said cramps were normal. This should be normal then. No need to worry. It seems like a lot of blood for normal. But *he* said, the *doctor* said the baby would be fine, even with the unusual cramping, that I just needed rest. *See, Lizzette? Just rest. It will help.* That's what I whisper to myself as my vision turns fuzzy and black creeps at the edges. *Rest. Normal…* I slip into darkness.

CHAPTER 1

I wish I'd kept that slip of paper. It was his signature move, sending his bodyguard with a note and number to the young women he had eyes on. Like sending a note to your crush in sixth grade asking, "Do you like me? Check yes or no." Except Rob's came with a catch—he could help me start a music career. When you're seventeen and dreaming of being a professional singer performing for packed crowds, an opportunity like this feels like a gift that just fell out of the sky. That whole "gift" part seems pretty ironic now.

If you think I told my story for money… *hahahahahahahaha.* Check yourself and start listenin' up. So far, opening up about my past has only brought me pain, broken relationships, and mistrust in the human race. I've lost jobs and friends, been threatened more times than I can count, called every name in the book, questioned my worth as a human being, came close to giving up on everything altogether, and found I can still stand. Judge away if you like. Everything was taken away and I'm still here.

***

At seventeen, my family moves us down to Miami Beach. I'm a senior in high school, ready to move onto bigger life things alongside my ride or die, my best friend Michella. We get each other. Both of us grew up in poor families where the lack pressured us to hustle, take the lead ourselves, and make our own money by any means. We do things to survive. I'm not always proud of how, but it's the only way to get by. No one else is gonna do it for us.

She works at the Aventura mall, so I go there a lot and wait for her to get off work. See what she can snag to resell. Like I said, not always proud, but we need basics: clothes that fit, backpacks without holes that can still carry books, something in the pantry that isn't alcohol or ramen.

It's a regular afternoon, and I'm lingering as usual, chatting with school friends, hanging out right in front of her stall. We've all been walking around. None of us have money, so it's "future life" window shopping until parents pick us up. That's when I see him. He's wearing sunglasses indoors, all-black athletic gear, and holding up one of those chunky Motorola phones to his ear. The guy walking beside him is maybe seven feet tall, intimidating as all get out, also dressed in black. The phone alone stands out. None of us have cell phones. We carry quarters in our pockets for the payphones by the movie theater.

I turn to my friend next to me and whisper, "Girl, that's *R. Kelly*."

"What? You crazy? Why would R. Kelly be at the mall?"

"I just saw him in concert, know what he looks like. It's him. I swear."

That last part he must have heard because he turns around to look at us. Well, maybe not *us*—he's looking me right in the eyes, a smile breaking across his face. No hesitation whatsoever, he walks right up to me and puts his arms around me, pressing me into a hug. Time freezes. I can't tell if my body is hot or cold. My limbs feel numb and lifeless but my face burns with heat.

R. Kelly takes a step away and says, "How are you?" Real smooth-like. "Not always around the area. I'm recording an album here."

"Oh," I squeak out, "Okay… that's nice."

"What's your name?"

"Lizzette. I go to school close by and we were just…" my mind is blanking, "…waiting." *Lame, Lizzette, come on.*

"Nice meeting you," he says, going in for a second hug. Then he turns and walks away.

We're all at a loss, standing there in awed silence when the bodyguard turns and walks back, but he passes us. I can hear him in the store to our left, asking for a piece of paper and a pen. Striding back out, he hands me a slip of paper with a phone number and says, "R. Kelly would like you to call him." Just me. Singled out.

He walks off as I stand there, unmoving, like a dumb rock, mouth dropped open, hand still up in the air where my fingers accepted the slip.

Michella comes out from an employee area and stares at me, stuck in this position, still as a statue. "What are you doing?"

"R. Kelly just gave me his phone number."

"Um, okay."

"Weird, right? I'm not gonna call."

Out of the mall and back in reality, I have zero intention of calling the number on the sales receipt. The black and white scribble taunts me, though, with this tiny sliver of hope. Everyone around me seems more excited about it than I am. My feelings are conflicted. How often does someone famous just drop their digits to a stranger in a mall? And he's older. Quite a bit older. It seems a little odd that a twenty-eight-year-old wants to give a kid like me the time of day, much less potentially offer up his own time to invest in my future. Little sketch if I'm being honest.

But my family needs help. Badly. For godsakes, we're basically living in someone's backyard. If I become successful, I can finally give my parents the support they never were able to offer me. Watching my parents struggle my entire life has left this shadow that lurks behind every decision, every push forward, every response to opportunity. Current situation is weird, no doubt, but if it can lift my family out of poverty… I could go with weird.

Michella's been there through everything. She's got my back even when I don't, so we bounce the idea—and everything that comes with it—back and forth. Which means I do everything I can to try and back out of the whole thing.

"Well," Michella draws all her words out, like she's thinking hard about what to say next. "I think you should call. You know, you really can sing, and he helped Aaliyah back in the day. He was her mentor, and it looks like it helped her a lot. Look where she's at now. That could be you." I heave the biggest sigh possible as she steers me to the phone, saying, "Lissie, this could be your big break. You better call him or I'm gonna call for you."

Lifting the phone from its cradle, she holds it up to my face, dial tone thrumming. "At least give it a try." She punches in the numbers quickly and presses the cold plastic into my hand. I hold my breath at the trill sounding in my ear.

"Heyyy." Oh god, I about drop the phone. His voice is smooth as can be, sliding up my arms and settling into my skin. And I'm nervous—like a little kid—stammering and all. I don't know what to say. Will he even remember me? Ugh, I feel dumb.

"Hey, R.—R. Kelly? It's Lizzette. I don't know if you remember me… the girl you just met at the mall…" My words stumble as I try to collect myself. "No?" There's slow breathing on the other side but no response so far. "You gave me a hug? Two, I guess." My breath sucks inward in embarrassment as I wait for any sign of recognition in the loaded silence, hands trembling. Michella leans closer.

It takes a second. To my relief, his voice finally rumbles into the phone, "Oh yeah! Wit' the pretty eyes! I *just* met you at the mall. Yeah, I know, you the *real* pretty one." A generic compliment, but I'll take it. I glance at Michella, her eyes are fixed on me as she tilts her ear toward the phone, her head almost touching mine. At least she's getting a kick out of this. I can't think of a response, so I say nothing. Michella turns to give me a look and jerks her head at the phone, but nothing worth saying comes to my brain. He again breaks the awkward silence. "Okay. Well, we at Sports Authority right now. Can you come? We're gonna go eat pretty soon. I want you to come eat with us, dinner with me and the guys. And we could talk about, you know, everything."

What the fuuuu.... Did he just say that? Immediate internal reaction is glaring uncertainty. This cannot be real. R. Kelly wants to meet for dinner? Not at the studio. Is this a career move too? Maybe he wants to get to know me first— get a better idea of my background, style, how I get along with people. My trailing thoughts are interrupted when Michella nudges me to bring me back to earth, head shaking up and down hard as she mouths, "Go. Say yes." At my dirty look, she throws a slight eye roll and whispers, "You're not going alone, dummy."

"Fine," I mutter into the phone. "I mean, yes! That sounds good. We're going to get a ride there. We'll go. My friend and I, I mean." *Little rambling but voice is steady. He probably can't tell you're terrified.* "My friend is coming with me." He wants to know how far away we are. Maybe thirty... forty-five minutes? Wow, still wants to meet. Here we go, I guess. My hand scribbles down the words "Sports Authority" for no reason, with a shake that almost makes it illegible, and I hang up. A second of silence ensues, followed by both Michella and I jumping up and down screaming.

"C'mon!" Michella is dancing down the hall. "I'm doing your hair and makeup, because, you know, we need you to look *good.*" Insufferable best friends always knowing exactly what to do. "This is it, girl." She starts poking me everywhere, little jabs as I twist and turn away with a huge grin. "And you better sing!" Ah, that. She knows me too well. Despite singing being the dream and joy of my life, my shy side is known to take over sometimes when it's just me solo. She's right, though. This is an opportunity I can't afford to lose.

Since I can never seem to handle my own hair, Michella always does it for me. Au natural is usually my vibe. In other words, not dealing with it is my style. Most days it's beach hair. Maybe looking a bit ragged, but, whatever. It's got character. She's up for the challenge because she's my protective mother hen, and there's no way that girl is going to let me go alone or not looking damn fine for the occasion. Her hands had started fussing with my locks the minute that phone clicked back in its cradle. This girl is magic.

Once Michella finishes applying my makeup and shoots me a quick reprimand about not touching my face, I pull on a pair of denim shorts and tan wedge sandals, prop a brown newsboy cap at just the right angle, and finish the outfit off with an open mini vest. While she works on getting herself ready, there's finally time to examine myself in the mirror. I look *good*.

We ain't rich girls. Our parents can't pay for new clothes, so we steal from Michella's work and sell them to friends. If we didn't, I probably wouldn't have clothes that still fit. We also don't have a car, but we have our own ride system set up. Kids at our school are wealthy. They're not just driving any old car around, but expensive cars paid for by their parents. My Puerto Rican classmate, Vic, has one of the flyest cars out there. He seems to have a crush on me, and he's one of the people we call up on the regular when we need rides. It's not one-sided; we're all friends.

Outside the living room window, grey skies are making the yard into a lake due to pouring rain. Bit of a downer for our fresh outfits—so we call Vic and beg him to chauffeur us to Sports Authority to meet an important guy for dinner.

He sounds a little offput by the request but agrees anyway. "I guess the rain is pretty bad… I'll come pick you guys up."

Vic arrives in a Crown Vic. This Crown Victoria is gorgeous, all souped up with flashy rims and other enhancements. As the car pulls to a stop at the curb out front, our friend, Ramone, lowers the front passenger window, waving hello with a still-smoking blunt.

Despite the glamorous exterior, our ride reeks of pot, and I don't smoke. Everyone but me hits the blunt the whole way there. They're probably on number two by the time we're halfway there. Worry creeps in on my excitement. What if R. Kelly smells marijuana on me? What would he think? Would he judge me because I'm in high school and my clothes smell rank from drugs? These thoughts and more have my nerves on the brink of snapping by the time we arrive at our destination. Thankfully, the rain over here is just a few scattered drops. Circling the parking lot and not seeing anyone waiting outside the store for us, Vic brings the car to a full stop. I push open the door, and *whoosh*. Pungent smoke visibly billows out with me. Nice. Mortified, I slam the door behind me. *Why did I even come here? I'm with this guy who smells like a freaking drug dealer. I mean, he might be. And it doesn't matter, but now all R. Kelly's friends will be making assumptions about me and probably so will he…*

Still hyped up, an incessantly chattering Michella slips off the pot-saturated seats. I swing her door shut behind her to keep the rest of the cloud in, and we turn around to face our most exciting life moment yet. Which turns out to be staring in wonder at a nearly empty Sports Authority parking lot. A couple coupons and crumpled receipts drift across the asphalt and stick to puddles left by the recent downpour.

"Jesus," I whisper aloud. "He wanted to meet me *here*?" Realization dawns and I'm not sure whether to feel silly or proud. Of course, we're meeting in the middle of a vacant parking lot. I'm a kid. If he picked me up from my house, my parents would be involved and neighbors would see. Not to mention, directly meeting at the restaurant would make my high school status really obvious when I got dropped off by Vic. It seems it would even be suspect to meet up *inside* the store. Anyone could see, and you never know who's around.

Michella turns to me, eyebrow raised. "You know why he wanted to meet you here." Yes, but *parking lot.* Why not just list cross streets?

We walk towards a couple cars with a bunch of guys lingering about, draped on hoods, leaning out of passenger doors, and standing around talking. Unsure if it's the right crowd, we keep heading towards the entrance of Sports Authority.

"'Ey, Shorty!" A voice calls out, "I'm over here!" In my nervous state, I'd walked right past him. *Oh my god. I didn't even recognize him! Lord, Lizzette. Really?* I flip around quick to try and redeem the moment.

"Oh hiiiii." I throw in a slight giggle.

R. Kelly is walking towards me and my chest feels like bursting with nerves. Vic and Ramone, still in the parked car, look dubious about the whole scene. They're staring at us like, *You girls straight? Should we actually leave you here?* They wait in the car looking unsettled for a minute until Michella waves them off. With two quick nods, they bolt.

"Nice to see you again... R. Kelly," I mumble. Way to be awkward already.

"It's Robert, or Rob, and it's good to see you too. Glad you came."

There's a Mercedes Benz Convertible with "12PLAY" license plates and an older guy sitting in the back. Rob motions for me to get in the front while Michella scootches into the back next to someone introduced as Rob's cousin, Mack, who is clearly thrilled about his new seatmate. Glancing in the rearview mirror, I can just barely see Michella's stony face recoil as Mack murmurs softly to her and settles his chain around her neck, tweaking it straight at her collarbones. I almost laugh as she shakes her head and hands it back.

Turning forwards in my seat again, my mouth falls open. There's a TV screen in the car. I've never seen anything like it before. My dad drives a Nova. When I start fiddling my hand along the underside of the seat to angle it up more, Rob stops me.

"No, darling, there's a button." I flush and look for said button. He's trying to lean across me to point. "You gotta, yeah, push the button."

"Oh… ok." The flush in my face glows warmer. What am I doing here?

As we get out on the main thoroughfare, Rob starts playing his own songs on the sound system, says he's working on a new one called "You Remind Me of My Jeep." His eyes hardly ever hit the road. Instead, they focus on me as he sings, "You remind me of something… can't think of what it is…" The constant turning away from traffic and closing his eyes to sing is flattering, but also worrying. "It's something about your love that's got me going crazy."

Leaving fear behind, all I can think in the moment is that this is really nice.

We pull into the parking lot for my first flashy meal out with the famous R. Kelly: Outback Steakhouse. Like anyone with authority who doesn't like being bothered with the small things, Rob sends his people inside ahead of us to find a table that fits everyone. As we wait, he continues singing, bobbing around me, showing off.

When we're waved through the door to go take our seats, several friends from school are working the front of house and look shocked to see Michella and I. As we pass, one girl brushes alongside me to whisper, "What are you doing here with him?"

"Mind ya business."

She replies with a shrug and keeps moving. I focus on keeping my cool, unaffected persona even as I slide into the booth and Rob slides right beside me, his knee touching mine. Michella is on the other side with Mack and a man introduced as Barry Hankerson, Rob's manager.

Rob leans in. "So, you're a singer."

"I'm a singer... I'm seventeen and finishing up high school this year." The small talk about ourselves is dry and quick. Every once in a while, I throw a glance at Michella, who is clearly thwarting Mack's advances with eye rolls and a stoic expression. Rob leans into his elbow toward the table center to include her in our conversation.

"So what female artist do you guys really like?"

Michella darts her eyes to mine as I drag out, "Weeeeeell... Mariah?" Brief surprise flashes across his face, but it's gone immediately. I already know he was expecting me to say Aaliyah. I recently heard rumors claiming they were together, and it felt wrong to be bringing it up before he had a chance to really introduce himself. It's still only rumors and talk as far as I know (which is pretty much nothing). I do love Aaliyah as only a true fan is capable, but I do not want to bring up anything controversial right away. "Yeah," I keep going, "I love me some Mariah Carey."

A beat of silence, then Rob breaks into a short laugh, "Oh, ok. Yeah." People around the table participate with slight nods and half smiles until...

"Didn't you MARRY Aaliyah?" Dear, bold Michella opens her mouth and suddenly *everyone* at the table has somewhere to look other than in our direction. Repressing the urge to crawl beneath the table and die of shame on this first meeting out, I keep my hands clasped between my knees and shoot her a hard look. Of all things. Fair question, to be sure, but right now? We're brand new to this group.

Instead of acting angry or offended, Rob breaks into a smile that somehow smooths over the entire rift. "Don't believe everything you read." He's so calm and unworried it's hard to believe the marriage whispers could be true. "If anyone knew, it would be this man right here." He points at his manager. "This here is Barry Hankerson. Aaliyah is his niece." Michella is temporarily stunned into silence.

The tension starts to dissolve as we go around and order food, and Rob slides his hand onto my thigh, underneath the table. Rubbing his hand over my leg, a cold tickle snakes down my back. I can't tell if it's excitement, unease, or something else entirely.

"Yeah, we want to hear you sing!" I'm broken out of my fog of discomfort by Rob's voice. Everyone at the table is staring at me. I'm uncertain now if this is a dream or a nightmare.

CHAPTER 2

"Oh… um, good! Yeah, that sounds fun. We should do that soon—totally," is my lame response at the prospect of going to a professional studio with a known music artist. Terror does that to you.

"Great. We'll head to the studio after we eat."

Oh shit. We're going to the studio.

"Michella!" My whisper is harsh and breathy in her ear as we all start getting up from dinner.

"What?"

"I can't. I can't go to the studio."

"Just call your mom. It'll be ok. I'll be right there. This is what you've been waiting for all this time. Let him hear you." Does turning eighteen somehow give you this new confidence? Michella isn't much older than me, but she seems so calm and collected, like she's in control and has everybody in check. I hope this magically happens to me when I "officially become an adult."

Our group starts sliding out of seats and pushing back chairs, claiming coats, stuffing away wallets, and pulling purses over shoulders. Suddenly everyone else in the restaurant notices R. Kelly. *Oh my gawwwwwwwwd, do you see who that is? Look!* The voices come from all directions. Untrained in the art of being around celebrities in public, my eyes are darting towards each sound, taking in the chaotic shift in atmosphere as fans start shuffling closer to see. People stand up, fishing for cameras and making loud comments.

"Don't look at them." Rob's hand guides me away with the rest of the group, then drops. "Just keep going. Keep your head down. Let's go." The second we're outside, the guys all bust out laughing and race to the parking lot. Confused, I jog after them, but only figure it out once we're flinging open the car doors. No one paid. All these guys think it's hilarious.

Retaking our spots in the car, Rob turns up his own stuff again for the second ride. We're headed to the Hit Factory Criteria Studios and I can hardly breathe. I am so excited. Anyone who is anyone knows about the Hit Factory and has recorded there. All kinds of artists. Rolling Stones. Everybody. Any place that has the Bee Gees as a solid fixture for years deserves recognition.

Walking inside is a dream come true. I've never been in a place like this, never seen anything like it. Impressed would be an understatement—more like elated but terrified. This is where I want to be. Studios line the halls as though they stretch out forever. Nice ones. So nice I'm afraid to touch the doorframes, much less go inside and fiddle with the equipment. Gold and platinum albums hang in rows along the walls.

Right away, Mack is leading my best friend past the doorway where Rob gestures for me to come with him into a recording studio. He grins at me. "Come in here. I'm gonna play you some piano."

Michella looks pissed but she's clearly not included in the invitation. With Mack's arm around her shoulders, she calls back, "Okay, sure, I'll be in the next room over." But he's already guiding her away with the rest of the crew, trying to fit his chain over her again as they walk to a separate chillout room where there's a TV, games, and other things to pass the time. I follow Rob alone into a recording studio.

I'm so nervous.

It's magnificent. Once you walk through the control room, with so many electronics it looks like something out of a futuristic film, there's the live room, which is spacious and bright. An elegant piano rests in the corner, microphones are scattered throughout the space, and beautiful wood hangs on the walls for acoustic purposes. My face must be so fucking red. I'm glad I can't see myself. In the back of my mind, I'm wondering what time it is. If I'm not home by nine, there's hell to pay, but there's no way I'm leaving here now.

Rob eases himself in front of the piano, looks at me, then the empty space beside him, so I let my trembling legs lower me onto the bench within inches of where he sits. With a flourish, he dives straight into his own songs. I've heard rumors about his talent, but they didn't prepare me for this. His natural musicality is incredible. The movement in his work is strong. In my head, I'm freaking out. He is *everything*. It's impossible to not just sit and stare, shifting back and forth between taking in his hands on the keys and the emotions on his face.

We've been in the room about forty-five minutes—me dazed in fangirl awe—when he casually brushes his hand over my leg for the second time. I panic and push it away. Refocusing on the piano, he starts playing a Boyz II Men song and asks me to sing for him. Oh my god. I don't sing for just anyone at any time. It's too nerve-wracking when I don't have the stage and the lights and other girls supporting me. My throat goes dry.

When my mouth drops open and no sound comes out, R. Kelly dips his head and starts kissing me—hard. I don't move. My body is frozen. His mouth presses roughly against my lips, and suddenly his tongue is in my mouth. No one has ever kissed me like this. This is new. When it's clear I'm not kissing back, he pulls away and returns to his music. Getting nervous it'll happen again, I take a deep breath and begin to sing with him. Nodding along, a smile breaks out and his hands slide off the keys to rest on his knees as he tells me I've got stuff going for me and we should write music together to get a track going soon.

"I had fun with you, Zette. I'd like to kick it with you."

Excitement bursts in my chest as my heart starts pounding at the thought, and I know he can see it in my eyes. He can also tell I'm antsy and keep checking the clock behind his head. The terror of breaking curfew with my mother is real.

"I'm so sorry, not ignoring you," I rush to explain, "I have a curfew. I actually have to get home soon."

"No worries. I'm usually up all night working on music if you ever wanna stay."

"All night?"

Rob grins. "Night owl. Best work happens at night, so my workday's just starting." He fiddles with the keys before turning back to me again. "I want you to come back tomorrow." Um, what? "Do you have a swimsuit?"

Once again, um, what? "…Yes?"

"Do you know how to swim?"

"Yeah, why? Do you know how to swim?"

"Nope. You can teach me."

Oh god, first I'm invited to the studio and now I'm heading to the pool with him?

Rob walks me out front where Michella continues to reject his cousin Mack. The man is all over her with attention. He's grinning with these widespread teeth, and she's turning away, slightly putting up an elbow, or rolling her eyes at every little attempt. Rob picks up a basketball and starts shooting as he breaks out into his own rendition of Blackstreet's "Before I Let You Go," stealing a few glances in my direction to see if I'm watching. This time I roll my eyes. Such a player. Really, though, inside I'm smiling so hard. I want to hold onto this moment: lingering outside as night rolls in with Rob singing to me loud and clear. Until he stops and turns to his bodyguard, Big John.

"Take them home." And he does.

Back in our own neighborhood, Michella and I thank the driver and whisk ourselves off the slick, leather seats and into her house with a final wave. Beelining to her bedroom, we squeeze the door shut behind us and look at each other. Then we start screaming.

"Oh my Gawwwwd!"

"What the hell is going on!!"

"I don't knowwww!"

"Also, where were you? What happened?" she asks me. Beneath Michella's elation there's a spark of panic and worry in her eyes. "They took me to this other room to just hang out and I kept asking over and over, 'Where's Lizzette? I want to see my friend.' They just kept saying, 'Whatever, leave her alone. She's with Rob. Leave her alone.'" She shrugs uncomfortably. "It felt like they were trying to keep us separated."

I tell her what happened on the piano bench.

"Ugh, I don't know, Lissie. I know it's a great opportunity for you, but he's kinda, like… he's creepy."

"Yeah, I know." I consider this for a second, "but hanging out with him is kinda like hanging out with our friends from school. He's kind of a creep—I mean it's creepy, acting like one of the kids—but then you relate to him for it. I forget he's older when I'm with him. It feels like it's from the heart. He basically *is* a kid, talking all young and everything. Almost like he didn't grow up." Michella's mouth twists into a frown but she says nothing, just looks at me for a long time.

CHAPTER 3

Once I'm home from dinner and the studio, I can't sleep. We were dropped off at Michella's because I don't want my mom to see no man dropping me off. Mom and I are already getting into it a lot. My parents' financial situation seems to be deteriorating all the time, so we live in a little studio in the back of a house that belongs to a grumpy, elderly woman named Gladys.

I know families have issues even when they *can* close doors and breathe in their own space. We have one room. There is no space. My stepdad, mom, brother, and I are all trying to live life while crammed in this tiny area where we're practically stepping on each other's toes just going to the fridge. To make life even harder, Mom is going through "the change." Everything bothers her, so I tell her almost nothing about my life. This is why when I get home and my mom asks what we ended up doing, I brush it off—tell her we went to the mall. I ain't lying after all.

The sole phone for the entire property is inside Gladys's house, so we can't take calls without a timely heads-up and permission. Gladys owns the phone. This was made absolutely clear early on. If a friend, cousin, policeman, or whoever calls, you still have to go through the lady of the house. She would always irately yell into the receiver, "Who is this?!" It's a great way to strike the fear of God in people and dissuade them from ever calling back.

Anyway, he calls—Rob calls—asking for me. How he has my number is a mystery to me. Did Michella's mom give it to him? Probably didn't even realize it wasn't someone she knew. My mom is always drunk, and Michella's mom is always drunk. They've been drunk for fifty years. Not their fault, though, at all. Both suffered abusive childhoods at the hands of raging alcoholics.

Naw, none of us are blaming them—they've got their own trauma to deal with, their own ghosts, their own lingering emotional walls and nightmares. I don't get along with my mom, but I feel for her. Every time I hear a story about her past, I wanna hug her, but I know after everything that happened, she just wants to be left alone. The oldest of ten, she took care of the other kids, and took the brunt of residual anger from her father while handling the household. That kind of shit ruins something inside you. Creates a cycle. Cycles are nearly impossible to stop because we all learn from each other.

Anyway, the only reason I know Rob called is because the day after he calls, Gladys bumbles over to the shared studio to tell my mom.

"Were you aware there's a man calling for your daughter?"

Ohhhhhh shit. Life is turning on me real fast. My first instinct is to run and not stop until I get to another state, maybe another country, like Canada. I can get used to the cold.

Mom's hands automatically fly to her hips. "Who is it, Lissie?" My mom may be drunk, but she sure isn't stupid. She can smell a snake a mile away.

"No idea."

Gladys's creaky voice jumps in again, "Yeah, he wouldn't give his name, but you know you can't get phone calls here." The evil eye she gives me could scare an angel up in heaven all the way from here.

I can't believe my life. So embarrassing. R. Kelly, *the* R. Kelly, calls and is told by a snappy old woman I'm not even related to that I can't answer the phone here because we live in the backyard without a phone line. It stings deep because it's more than that. It shows what kind of life I have. Can't have friends over. Can't be by myself. Can't even have someone try to contact me. I'm sure Gladys got deep joy out of telling him off, she seems pretty pleased with herself right now.

Michella catches me at school to make sure it's clear she has no intention of being the go-between for this friendship.

"You don't understand," she complains. "He called and then he sent someone to my house! Askin' about you and all. I told 'em your parents are stupid strict and if he wants to work with you, he needs to talk to them." She lifts her hands in frustration. "I thought he was using that info to actually make things right and get this career going for real. Look, talk to your mom so this stuff can get started already."

"My mom wasn't even the big deal. Gladys wasn't warned, and he called her place and I got in trouble! Now my parents are asking who the mystery guy is that's calling for me. Him not leaving any details with Gladys came across a little shady. He definitely did not try to stop by and meet my parents."

"Just call him back. He said he really wants to bring you to the studio again."

"Really?" The tension in my chest melts away at the thought of going back.

I call Rob that afternoon, but it doesn't start out quite as nice as I intended.

"Hello?" his voice flows low and confident through the phone.

"Man, you can't just call my house like that unless you want to talk to my parents! Everything goes through them. *And* Gladys. The crazy lady who owns the house."

Other than the slight buzz coming over the line, there's only silence. A low cough sounds. "...I don't really talk to parents. Parents don't usually like me."

My turn for uneasy silence.

He keeps going, though, "You know, there's still the pool here at the house if you can come by. The one I mentioned before. If you want to. We could work on writing some music while you're here. Then head to the studio."

Releasing a deep breath, I spiral the phone cord around my finger. Is this a good idea? Doesn't matter, I give in. "I don't have my own car, so where exactly is the house? Like is it hard to get to, 'cause I can ask a friend to take me but then I'm not going to ask them to leave."

Exasperation echoes heavily in his voice. "I'm not really okay with that. I can already tell your friends talk too much and I'm a private person. I don't need or want all my business out there for everyone."

Guess I'm figuring out how to go alone.

Since it's my business too, I at least tell my girl, Michella. Can't just be going alone to a guy's house with no one knowing. Plus, I've known him, what? Five days or something? Maybe less.

"So where is this house?" She eyes me hard as I try to act casual. With a sigh, she starts rummaging in her stuff, pulling out paper and a stubby pencil. "You got to give me the address, *and*," a pause for emphasis, of course, "you got to call me when you get there. Deal?" I nod. "How you getting there?"

So suspicious, all the time.

"They're coming to get me."

"*They*?" It's like being interrogated, but instead of more demands, she nudges my shoulder. "Okay, just remember that you're calling me. Be safe."

Big John picks me up on the corner outside my high school and we drive to a place by Miami Beach on Chase Avenue and 41st. The house isn't extravagant like I expected, but it's pretty, with an art deco vibe and a large pool in the back. As I'm walking up, a stubby pug charges out to meet me but ends up contentedly licking my knees. Aw, he has a dog too? Yes, that's my self-reassurance he's a solid person. Grasping at straws…but it's something.

Walking inside the house, Blackie waves hello and shuffles over to greet me while the pug chases my ankles.

"Twelve Play," he directs this at the dog, "be nice, 'kay?"

Twelve Play scrambles around my feet as Rob's bodyguard wanders back in to grab a drink from the fridge. In no time at all it's just Rob and I out back—the other two choosing to lounge in the cool, indoor air-conditioning. I'm thrilled to be outdoors in the cool water. It feels incredible right now to swim back and forth, stretching myself out in the sunshine. Paddling to the edge, my elbows dig into the bricks as I hoist myself up to shout at Rob.

"I thought you wanted to learn how to swim," I call out, because he's still sitting on the pool deck, relaxing in a chair without swim trunks or anything, just watching. He's not even remotely attempting to get ready for swimming.

"Nah. I like to watch." A cheeky smile spreads across his face. "I'll just watch you." He winks and relaxes into the lounging position again.

We spend the afternoon by the pool, but as evening starts to settle in, Rob jumps up, stretching his shoulders and shaking out his arms. "I gotta go to the studio. Work to do!"

"Man, I have to go home. I thought we were heading to the studio tomorrow to start writing things."

"I told you. I work best at night. Can't change that." Settling onto the lounge chair next to me, he bumps my knee playfully with his. "We'll talk about it, Zette. Whatever works. We'll do it. You gonna be big. Promise."

It's hard to not believe him, he seems so chipper about it. This night studio thing is kind of a downer since I'm only seventeen and have an early curfew for school. I want to be at the studio with him; it's the whole point. I can hardly hide my disappointment as I dip my head and fasten my sandals. It seems like something always stands in the way of my vocal career. I guess I have to put my trust in him that he'll continue to be my bridge into that world. There's no one else who can.

CHAPTER 4

My first attempt at being a recording artist started out promising and then crumbled away into fine, fine dust. I was singing in a group with two other young women who were both incredible. As in, I felt lucky to be included. I had won a singing contest on the radio station, Power 96. The win sent my parents on an all-expenses-paid vacation in the Bahamas, but it also meant someone noticed I could sing and put me in touch with a manager who came to meet me and my family. It all sort of fell together right away. Probably because you know you need to jump on it when you have any reasonable opportunity that might hit. You never know when it's gonna happen again.

This manager took us to the studio, paid for everything, and he even took us to a concert. He said he wanted us to see what it was like—the structure, how the openers build up to the headliner, what creates the right vibe, how people respond, and what the performers do to engage the audience.

I'd never been to a real concert. Genuinely expected my parents to say no, but they didn't. R. Kelly was headlining, but we were going to this particular show because our manager wanted us to see the opening female acts, so we could start getting an idea of how we should appear onstage.

The show was great. Lots of screaming, dancing, and crazy lights. After it ends, we're standing there with our manager, and one of R. Kelly's hype men comes out, floor level, carrying a large paper sign.

"HOT GIRLS COME BACKSTAGE. ANY AGE."

Hype guy and my manager make eye contact and give each other a nod. I didn't want to go back there. Also, my parents would kill me if I did. They made me cut ties with that manager soon after the concert. I found out he was dating one of the girls in our group, Janette. This girl could sing like Mary J. Blige. No joke. But he was having an affair with her. Nothing to do with underage issues or parents not liking him, she was older than us, twenty or so. Her decisions were hers alone to make.

I thought he was creepy, but that's just me. It felt like he had a crush on all of us at once. When he asked to take me out to eat, my parents' immediate response was, "Only if Janette's going." Guess my mom got a weird feeling too. Dinner night arrives and we go out to eat—my manager, Janette, and I—at the chicken place in Hallandale.

During the meal, they start bickering, so we finish up a little faster as it's turning into a full-blown relationship showdown. Right after walking out the door, as we step off the curb toward the car, Janette makes a snappy remark and he punches her. No warning, no split second to react. Full on punches her right in front of me.

My brain is fizzling. What the fuuuuck. What is going on here? We're in the ghetto-est place ever and I don't know what to do. It's just us, and he just popped her. I was poor, but I didn't grow up like that. If anyone had ever put a hand on my mom, she'd straight up kill them. That's just how she was. No one in our family was hanging around at home getting beat up by the men. This was new to me, and it scared me.

I didn't even try to hide it from my mom when I got home. I told her and my stepdad in a frantic rush of words the second I got inside the house. They were pretty damn clear about their feelings regarding it.

"Listen, your little career with him is *over*."

I was fifteen, almost sixteen. Musical aspirations already crushed once.

Another opportunity walks into my life when I'm on the beach with my sister, who's back for spring break from university in New York. Smart one in the family. Scholarships. Blah blah blah. The whole shebang. So, we're walking on South Beach, and this one guy catches our attention. He's super loud, animated, definitely has some Puerto Rican heritage in there like us, and my social butterfly sister doesn't lose a second in engaging him in conversation. Turns out his name is Tito Puente Jr. and his father is a professional musician. A legend, really.

He offers to take us home, and my sister immediately accepts the invitation. Mind you, he's still a stranger to me. How do we know it's really him? Uncertain, I follow her into his car (I know, and she's supposed to be the smart one), and he (thankfully) actually takes us home, then comes inside with us to meet my parents. They are over the flippin' moon.

Previously unknown to us, they idolize his dad's work. Tito Jr. is currently making music too, so he offers to do a record with me when he hears I can sing. It's a fun time. Like we have crazy fun. He comes over every weekend, and we dance and go all insane with our passion for music, having a freaking blast. My parents trust him, especially with his openness to be at our house. They're thrilled I'm doing music with him instead, and he starts to feel like a new member of the family.

On a break one day, us two pile into his car to get something to eat, and end up at a café of some kind, sitting in a booth opposite each other. We've been chatting the whole time as we usually do, mainly about music, but out of nowhere it moves into the future and dreams and such. With a smile, he reaches into his pocket, pulling out a plastic ball with a lid, and hands it to me. It's one of those toys from a gumball dispenser, where you crank the quarter and hope you get what you want when your prize falls out the bottom. I crack open the brightly colored lid and rip open the tiny bag.

It's a ring. A plastic ring.

"Wow. A ring. You ask my parents yet, mister?"

Tito laughs as he leans in. "Do you think your parents would let you marry me after you turn eighteen?"

"Uhhh. Probably *not*. I don't know… why would they?" My brain is floundering for words. Any words. I'm not used to any kind of flirtatious attention and I turn red as I get flustered. "But I don't like you like that! Also, you're *old*."

Tito laughs it off, but I find myself being awkward sometimes. Could someone older even like me? The thought is intriguing but terrifying.

Good things never last, though, and something comes up before we can actually start recording the music we've been working on. There we go again. Another lost opportunity. How do you find one that sticks?

A few days later, I'm walking down the street with my dad. He seems frustrated, breathing heavier and looking around and all.

"I hate walking with you." He doesn't even look at me when he says it.

"What?" I ask. "Why?"

"Because you have something about you that men, they just love. And I want to kill 'em all."

CHAPTER 5

I don't really have much going on after school other than a little side job, so it's easy to keep saying yes when Rob keeps asking. It does take a little maneuvering since my parents don't know about him yet and I don't have a car, plus it's nearly impossible to contact me directly. Somehow, we're making it around all those blockades. Secretly, it's exciting that he's putting in the effort to make it work.

He wants me to come to the studio again, and I'm not working the day after, so why not? It'll be just me this time. No Michella as defense if I need it. Her dance practices are in the afternoons, and being team captain and all, it's not really an option to skip out. I haven't even known him a full week yet, but this time we'll be at the studio, which is a safe, professional spot to be. It's like going to another job. I repeat this to myself whenever I'm unsure.

Thirty minutes after saying yes to the invite, there's a fancy car pulling up at the end of the block, out of view of my house, to take me away from my everyday life again. I pull open a glossy door and slide over spotless leather. Clicking the seatbelt, my eyes wander over my neighborhood. My reality. I realize I hardly know this man. I shouldn't be headed there alone, but I can't handle staying in that one room apartment smashed up with my family for one more minute. I'm suffocating and I need out. Not just for today, either, for days in general, for my future.

Rob is headed to dinner, so I'm meeting him at the restaurant. Excited at the possibilities, I stretch my neck to see out the window as the driver pulls up to... Bennigan's. Huh. Maybe it's his way of keeping expectations low or coming across as a normal guy. That's fair. It's a work relationship anyway.

Rob's demeanor at dinner is noticeably different this time around—more distant, polite, almost like he's trying overly hard to "act nice" or "put me at ease." It sets me slightly off guard. Maybe he has second thoughts about working with someone my age, or he knows I'm a virgin with zero knowledge about the world, or maybe he realizes how lost I am about starting my career and feels he should back up and take it slower. Ha, maybe he knows Michella will immediately tell her mom or call up the police if anything happens to me. She would not be having it. Yeah, she'd kill 'em.

At Rob's gesture, I slip into the front seat of his car as we're heading out instead of going with Big John. We arrive at a recording studio, but a different one. We're in the heart of the historical Art Deco District at the Marlin Hotel: South Beach Studios. The studio space itself is huge, the control boards are impressively giant, with more equipment stacked underneath, a whole board to the right just packed with colored wires, and a panel on the wall behind the sound chairs as tall as a person. There's an area off to the side with couches for lounging and watching films on the wall. Rob must have just had a birthday, because when we walk into the room, people are mingling and hanging out in between heaps of roses, bouquets, teddy bears holding puffy hearts, and a bunch of other gifts clearly sent by a flock of female admirers. Everything is marked to either "Rob" or "R. Kelly."

So yeah, I get a little nosy. Or we can just be nice and call it *curious*. Would anyone not be in this situation? While he's focusing on music from behind the glass of the recording room, I'm on the other side of the sound engineers, where there are couches, snacks, drinks, and a lava lamp. I sneak peeks at the scattered cards to see what they say. They're basically all from women: generic well-wishing, lots of hearts, a few dirtier ones mixed in here and there. A few comments go a little over my head. Telegrams are strewn throughout the pile too. I glance at the glass of the live room to see if Rob is watching, then lightly spread them around with the tips of my fingers to see the ones underneath. One card catches my eye.

"Happy Birthday! I love you! Your "little" Toni Braxton. XOXO." Forgetting about Rob entirely, my eyes stay glued for a second. Can't be. Toni Braxton's little sister—isn't she younger than me? Maybe the same age, but I don't think so. *Stop thinking about it.* I shake my head to forget, focusing on the hands of the sound guy as he flicks from one knob or button to another, nodding at the voice in his headphones and smiling occasionally in response.

The space itself is elongated, with the live room facing the sound engineers on one end, and the large, open relaxation area at the other. A bunch of Rob's usual buddies are playing around in the back area where I'm sitting. Yo' mama jokes flying off the wazoo. Every two minutes another one is thrown out there and they all bust out laughing. When it's not yo' mama jokes, it's pranks. I personally prefer the jokes, but all of it makes me laugh.

From the opposite side, Rob is gesturing for me to come closer, so I squeeze past people and join him. He's working on a song called, "I Can't Sleep Baby," and watching him nail the music in person is like being inside a dream. He's brilliant. No question there. He's not writing anything down and I know that other than voice technique, he's mainly self-taught, playing a range of instruments at a professional level.

Crooning at the top of the scale to show off impressive range, the song just magically comes out like silk until one of the lines makes zero sense and shatters the whole vibe.

He pauses to take notes and sing a recap under his breath. Same thing. Everyone in the room looks up then away simultaneously with similar cringey expressions. They're avoiding each other's eyes, trying to ignore the nails-on-a-chalkboard clash of words that don't make sense. At all. Everyone caught it.

I scan the room, waiting for someone to say something. Is no one going to tell him? He *can't* record it like that. It's so bad. Am I mistaken? Did no one notice? Some of the group appear to be holding their breath, just waiting for the moment to blow over before Rob realizes his mistake.

Leaning in behind the engineer's shoulder so he can hear me, I say, "Excuse me? Rob? That last line, the words didn't really make sense. It would sound better if you—" Cold, angry eyes lock on mine. In my defense, I knew Rob didn't read music, but I didn't know he was illiterate. I have no idea this is a source of contention and embarrassment until his face screws up in fury and he flings his hands up toward the ceiling.

"Oh yeah? Whatchu gonna want royalties now?" He shouts at me through the glass.

Completely taken aback, I can feel the tension of his friends around me. No one will look up at me. In an attempt to recover, I hear myself say, "No, I was just trying to help."

Rob stands in the open frame of the recording booth, his glare traveling around the room... daring anyone else to pitch in. My chest tightens as normally tough guys look at their shoes, the holes in their jeans, the clock, anything. They already knew how it would turn out. None of them wanted to lose their spot in the crew by speaking up. I'm about ready to dip out the of room forever when the engineer steps in.

"I'm sorry, Rob. She's right about the phrasing. I should have been the one to tell you. That's my bad." The strain in his voice makes it clear he didn't want to be involved, but I'm grateful he spoke up. He must feel *really* bad for me to be doing this. I'm getting the sensation that no one wants to upset Robert. Ever. They already know how it'll go down. Still, the humiliation crawls up my spine and flushes my face until it's burning hot. Between being young, awkward and shy, I can't quite cover how upset I am. Tears sting the corners of my eyes as I try to angle my head in any position that prevents them from giving me away by rolling down my face. *Don't blink. Don't tilt. Don't move.*

Rob stares at the engineer, then me, and softens. Setting down his headphones, he comes out of the booth entirely and pulls me onto a couch, eyes fixed on the floor. Everyone else seems to find places to be. He takes my hand.

I realize there are people who don't know how to apologize. They know it's necessary for life, for people to move on and all that, but it doesn't quite make sense to them. They're not sure how to go about it. It's like if they admitted wrongdoing, it would hurt them too much instead. Instead of addressing the problem, they act nice, cover it up, explain their side, their why, and use that as a substitute apology.

Rob talks *at* me, and I sit there feeling awful, biting my lip, trying to press the rambling excuses out of my ears, and focus on not crying. Clearly he feels bad, but this isn't helping. Nothing so far has any sort of apology in it. His words run up and down, explaining why I shouldn't have done what I did and what makes his response okay and how it's reasonable considering his past. It's honestly making it worse. This is messed up. And kinda mean. He knows I was trying to be helpful. Aren't we gonna be writing music together soon anyway? Will I be allowed to talk then?

Rob scoots closer and wraps his other hand around mine. Okay, if he's trying, I'll try too. But now he's gone silent. Uncertain how to break the awkwardness, I ask him about his family, and his mother. Where she's at. I'm not sure where the inspiration comes from, but in the quiet, it feels like the right thing to ask to get to know him. His whole body shifts at the question, so I look up into his eyes and repeat myself, asking if she's still wherever he grew up. It seems like a normal conversation starter. Move things along out of the discomfort while getting to know more about him. His hands squeeze mine tight. Painfully tight.

"It's funny," Rob murmurs, "I was just thinking about my mom today, ya know? She passed away before I really became somebody. Well... before I made it big." He pulls away and runs his hands down his legs nervously. Then the feelings just pour out—the way she believed in him, how his mom had cancer at the end, but they'd been, "as tight as a hand in a glove," small things about her life and what she looked like. His face glows at the memory of her, and tears roll when he admits his mother had been everything to him.

Here is this giant music artist with so much success piling up, but as he sits beside me, I hear the heartbreak of a child missing their mother something terrible. It's innocent, endearing, and honest. He tells me how much her loss hurt him and continues to mess with his emotions.

I mean, I get it. I feel the same way about my father, and he's still alive and kicking, just not around me. My dad's the first person I loved like that. The first person I adored. And his absence in my life is an ache that won't leave and constantly branches out into other parts of my life without me realizing it. I understand. Rob's mom was everything to him.

As he describes the situation, I start to see him differently. Not as a huge star, but as a wounded little kid, still stuck in their childhood pain. I feel bad. Maybe something bigger is wrong that's been ignored instead of treated. My instincts are already clicking in to protect him, help him, soothe the ache. He must see it in my face because his expression changes. His eyes consider *me* now, as though taking another look. Could just be a, "Wow, she's a nice person," but maybe finally sees there are people who care about him and not just the connection *to* him.

What started as a strained scene somehow ends with me genuinely interested in getting to know him beyond the stardom status. Not sure yet how close he lets anyone get. He seems complicated—at war with himself and everyone else one moment, reaching out and trying to connect the next. Despite the newness of it all, I want to get close. Not talk bullshit or trivial nonsense, but be an actual friend, understand what's going through his brain when we're working together. I realize as he pushes himself up off the couch that I'm not even upset anymore. All that's left is empathy. Everything else drained away during the conversation.

Nothing else dramatic happens the rest of the session. Rob must feel bad about snapping at me, because he asks me to stay a while longer and takes me home himself.

Then he goes to Chicago, but without telling me.

I find out Rob's gone after not hearing from him for a bit. Eventually he calls Michella's house, blaming the disappearance on an emergency and asking her to please let Lizzette know. Something about how he meant to call and not just vanish, but it happened too quickly. I guess, in a way, not contacting my house is fair—he already learned not to call Gladys's number. Michella says he wants to work with me at the studio when he's back in Miami. I'm excited to actually get down to business. We haven't worked on my music yet. He's like a little kid. You put the candy in front of him and... you know what I mean. All he wants to do is play.

Hopefully we can make this mentorship official by introducing Rob to my parents. This secret life is getting harder to keep as a secret. Once he's out and open with them, he can bring me around to introduce me to the music world. That would be bomb.

The last time he drove me home, he stopped the car two blocks away from my house to let me out. Michella's place can be a direct drop-off point, but not mine. Always two blocks away. I want to say it's because I've been avoiding explaining him to my parents, but it's not. Isn't helping younger musicians get started in the music industry pretty standard? He doesn't have to hang out with my parents, just let them know what's up so I can work with him more. So I can stop hiding.

That's the rule I should lay down: no more work until everything is established and out in the open so the undercover pressure ends. But I'm afraid I'll lose all of it, so it's hard to set demands. It's hard to turn him down. I'm intrigued, I need the help, and I appreciate his belief in me and my talent. It's kind of all that's keeping me going right now. He'll have to meet my parents at some point anyway if this continues. Right? You can't hide in the timeline of a teenage girl's life forever.

CHAPTER 6

Supposedly Rob actually did *have* to go to Chicago (just give me a second to look up public records to figure out exactly who was suing him at the time…). I didn't have any direct information, but you know when something ain't right. Rumors said Aaliyah was in trouble, or that she might be pregnant. Rumors also said someone else might be pregnant, or in trouble.

I already knew what Rob would say if I asked: "Don't believe everything you read." It's his catchall. It reassures against a thousand sins in a single sentence.

Of course, the gossip about me spread like wildfire at school after that first dinner. My friend's sister, Alexis, worked the host stand that night. So, *naturally*, nearly all my classmates knew about it by the next day when I showed up for class. It's not paparazzi, but it felt just as overwhelming. People I didn't even know asked me random personal stuff. Like, girl, why would I tell *you* that? Everyone and their mom it seemed wanted to know what the hell I was doing with R. Kelly at that goddamned Outback Steakhouse of all places.

Now I know it wasn't just me, going through that kind of stuff. I'd heard rumors, snippets here and there, but no one seemed to really know, so I blew it off. R. Kelly was taking me to dinner. He was excited about me. I got to call him Rob. He was going to launch my music career. These things were happening, solid, real, and that's all I really needed to know.

Isn't naivety fun?

The harder truth recently dropped into my lap while eating dinner with an old high school friend. After chatting for a bit, he paused, tilted his head to look me right in the eyes and said, "You know there was another girl at the same time, right? Real pretty girl, just like you, 'cept she was black and white." I concentrated on my plate, letting it sink in, willing my breath to stay slow. I couldn't even look up at him in that moment. Unfortunately for me, he kept going, "I used to take her in my car and drop her off at the mall, because, uh, he would give her money to buy lingerie."

Staring hard at my cutlery, willing the rock that had hardened in my chest to go away, I knew who he was referring to. Part of me had always known. She had also been underage. Christ, she was younger than me.

Despite his concerned frown (probably wondering if it had been good judgment on his part to tell me), he continued, "She'd buy lingerie at Victoria's Secret and then have me drop her off at that house on Chase Avenue. Not to be blunt, but I'm pretty sure you know the one."

Hell, Robert probably took her to the same restaurants. That was his MO, after all: Outback Steakhouse, McDonalds, Red Lobster. He was all over McDonalds; it was his thing. Money does not mean fancy. Or classy. Humiliation burns at me as I think about the servers, hosts, and bussers at all those regular spots, who were probably shaking their heads and feeling sorry for me. And I thought I was so lucky. Another girl at the same school at the same time, just a grade below me.

God, Rob was meeting girls *younger* than me.

CHAPTER 7

Family. It can be a blessing *and* a curse. Everyone knows that. Many of my experiences growing up seemed to take the latter path, but my aunt Carmen and I have a special relationship. She visits from New York with her brother, my Uncle Israel. They stay with my grandmother and do regular sunshine-y vacation activities to temporarily detach from the New York extremes of soupy heat and whipping cold. Pretty sure we're some kind of soulmates. People always mention how alike we look when they see us together.

When a sluggish spring break comes and goes without any word, I figure R. Kelly must be done with me. It's okay. I'm busy getting back on track with my classes and figuring out how to pull off my new chopped bob to school. The haircut was less my choice and more Michella's—she got tired of straightening it for me.

My aunt and uncle are on their usual semi-annual visit and decide one morning to coax me into playing hooky while I'm getting ready at my Grandma's house.

"You wanna go to the beach with us?" I hear my Aunt Carmen say. I stop stuffing bent-up notebooks in my backpack and look her squarely in the eyes to make sure she's not messing with me. Sure enough, she's got her serious face on, set like concrete. It breaks for a warm smile as she says, "Come on, just for today."

"Yes!" I drop my backpack on the floor and my stuff scatters. "Duh, I wanna go." Okay, so maybe I don't really need coaxing.

"Ha. Good, because you can. Don't worry, you're not going to get in trouble."

"Alright, but really, don't tell my mom." I'm already heading off to get ready and I can hear my aunt's happy laughter following me down the hall.

The three of us take the bus and, soon enough, we're walking in North Miami Beach Sunny Isles. A turquoise sea lies beside us, we're chatting like we haven't in ages, and it's such a relief to be away from school for a day. I needed this.

As the walk drags on in the sweltering heat, a slight chill creeps up my neck. That's weird. I look around. Cars amble by, tourists stop randomly to take pictures, moms push strollers with layers of kids and more beach equipment than you'd take to go camping for a week, locals walk their dogs. All normal here.

But I can't shake it. Someone is staring at me. I try to subtly peek down the sand towards the ocean, then glance behind me with a quick head shake like I'm just *really* enjoying my surroundings, casually take in as much as possible without turning my head. Nothing. But I can feel it all over my body like ants, that uncomfortable presence.

About twenty feet further on, I notice a BMW with a bunch of guys stuffed inside being loud, sticking hands out the windows, joking around. They're a block away, but I'm positive they passed us before. I saw them when I was looking around earlier. They must have pulled a U-turn to come back. Not exactly weird on a beach drive where people are shopping, finding parking, and trying to see the view. The car isn't far off but also not directly in front of me or heading towards me, which is good. I see it park— a Beacon Black BMW just sitting there. Faces inside are directed toward the beach, out the windows, but I can't make out anyone's features through the treated windows.

Trying to enjoy the time outside with my family, I shake it off. People can be so weird here. Who thinks they're cool in a fancy car driving next to the beach but not actually going to visit the beach?

With Aunt Carmen leading, we march our stuff over by the pier. I still have that off feeling, but we're not even on the street anymore. All I see are families with colorful umbrellas, couples awkwardly rubbing suntan lotion on each other, and those super fit people who for some reason always want to play volleyball or frisbee and show off their tan, muscular bodies as they leap into the air. I set my things down on the sand, strip off my coverup, and wade slowly into the water.

My aunt and uncle end up in a lively conversation with a psychic lady sitting nearby. I'm crouched further down where the sand starts to go damp, listening to their conversation, when my eyes graze over the psychic's head and spot a man pointblank staring at me from above the pier. He's black and baldheaded, sporting sunglasses and basketball shorts.

Holy shit, is that Rob? It looks like him from here, but here is too far away to tell, plus he's supposed to be in Chicago. Also, if it is him, why doesn't he just wave? Ya know, to acknowledge that I see him. It can't be, but I can't really go up there to find out. That could get awkward real fast. If it's not him, things could get far weirder or more dangerous really quickly.

I try to ignore them.

My aunt and uncle and I spend a solid two hours taking in the sun and floating in the water while we talk about life and school. Every once in a while, when someone else is talking, I let my eyes dart up there, to the pier, and see the figure still there against the sunlight. Waiting. Whoever this is, and whyever they're here, they've spent two hours in the hot ass sun just standing and watching. I casually swivel my head back and forth in a back float to see if there are any other swimmers remotely close. There are tons of people, but no one else directly in that line of sight. Is he from the parked car? Are all those other guys still waiting up there?

No, it doesn't fit. There's no way Rob could have known where I was. I'm not even where I'm supposed to be because I skipped school. And there's no way of randomly running into someone on this crazy madhouse of a beach. He would have had to follow me from the house, which is insane. There's a twinge of unease as it dawns on me that whoever it is clearly didn't prep for splashing in the waves. They weren't planning a beach trip.

As our group packs up, it starts raining, and when I look up again, the man isn't at his post on the pier anymore. Not far away from where he'd been standing, the car is still there, parked. We're haphazardly throwing things together to race to the bus, arriving just in time to slide into seats as it starts to pour outside. The only thing I can see out my window is a waterfall of rain. It would be impossible to make out a black car through the window in this.

Back at my grandma's house, I immediately call Michella to relate my crazy, conspiracy-theory thoughts. As soon as I say it's me, she heaves a sigh almost as big as when Rob calls her Michelle instead of Michella.

"Honey, oh my god. Were you at the beach today with your aunt and uncle?"

"Yeah, how did you…?"

"Rob's been calling here all day. Said he saw you with your parents at the beach, and I told him they weren't your parents, it's your aunt and uncle, but he kept calling and asking me over and over again, like, 'Where is she? Where is she!?' All frantic like. And I had to keep telling him, 'She's with her aunt and uncle. Like I said!' Then he kept repeating the same shit every time he called: 'Please have her call me.' I almost unplugged the phone."

Oh.

"Are you ok," she asks, "Were you in danger of some kind? Like, *what* is wrong?"

I don't know how to answer the first question, so I start with the last. "I have no idea. And I don't think I'm in danger?" *It was him.* He was lurking. Didn't want to come down because he thought he'd have to meet my parents. Why didn't he just wave or something? Any kind of generic signal to say hello, even from a distance. "But there was someone there… on the pier for nearly two hours. They were on the, on the phone, a lot…" My brain is scrambling to connect everything, "On that fishing pier. Just… staring at me."

"And you think that was Rob?"

"Black, wearing all black, sunglasses, basketball shorts."

"Oh shit."

"Yeah."

"And he didn't even approach you or nothing?"

"No." My voice sounds faint.

"Because he thought you were with your parents? That's weird. He's a weird one."

I start to laugh but choke on it and break into a hoarse cough. I'm still too shocked by the revelation. "Yes. I mean, yeah, I guess so."

"Creep or not, he needs to hear from you. Please call him before our phone goes off again. Also, you better call him before he dials Gladys and you get in real trouble."

We say goodbye to each other and hang up. I stare at the tan, shiny plastic of the phone, then sit on a kitchen chair and stare at it a little longer. This is crazy. Should I call him? It's too early in the day for that. He has a Chicago number so it's expensive to call before nine. If I don't call soon, though, he's going to keep calling Michella. Ugh, I don't want my grandma to have to pay for a Miami call to a Chicago number. It'll show up on the phone bill and then she'll know something's up. But I need to know for sure. I can make it quick.

First words out of Robert's mouth when he answers the phone and realizes it's me: "Lizette! Please, please come over today. I saw you at the beach and I didn't know what to say. You looked so pretty." The words stumble out so fast it takes a second to register. He's apologizing to me right, begging me to come over, like we're super close or something. R. Kelly. *R. Kelly* apologizing to me for not saying hello at the beach. Life is getting stranger by the minute.

"What were you doing," I ask him. I don't mean to sound accusatory, but I know it comes out harsh.

"I just happened to be driving…" Odd place to just be driving. "…um, over there by the water."

"Okay, why didn't you just wave or something? It was kinda weird to be honest. Freaked me out. I thought I had a stalker." And I'm maybe not entirely off on that whole stalker bit.

His voice dips as he mutters, "Because I thought those were your parents. Come on, you look just like that lady."

"That lady is my aunt. We're related."

"I didn't know."

"Okay? You still coulda come said hello. It's a public place." Even I can hear the annoyance pounding in my voice.

"Nah, you don't understand. I can't do that." His words sink into a pleading whisper. "Because, well, I'm much older than you."

"Since you're much older, you stood there in the sun at the hottest part of the day for two hours? People don't do that. It's…" I'm at a loss for words. I mean, *I* wouldn't do that—stand there in the hot-ass sun for two hours, no cover. Rob's already famous. He's got nothing better to do on a blazing afternoon in Miami than stare at a high school-aged female friend for hours on end? I mean, he could be doing anything else. He could be downing cocktails with someone who can legally drink. That's what I would be doing on a muggy day like today.

The desperation in his voice jolts me from my thoughts.

"Can you come to the house right now? Please? We can work. Get started on your stuff."

"No, I can't go to your house right this second," I say. It feels like I'm explaining this to a small child. "You still have to talk to my parents about us doing music. They're not going to just let me go and hang out all the time at a guy's house they don't know." Rob starts butting in, but I interrupt. "And you do all your studio time at night! I can't go to the studio tonight or most any night. I have school. I have to explain being out late to my parents or I get in trouble."

"Just come meet me and we can talk about it. We'll make a plan. Okay? We're gonna make a plan."

Despite still being semi-starstruck, the word "bullshit" still flies across my mind.

"You know what, Rob? I can't go today for me." I hang up the phone with a sinking feeling that I'm going to regret that.

CHAPTER 8

Rob calls Michella again the next day, trying to get ahold of me. Says he's at a buddy's house and wants me to come, can I please come so he can make it up to me. I call Vic to get a ride there. Lo and behold, Rob's not even there anymore. It's just a bunch of his friends slumped around the house, drinking. They let me use the phone to call him and he tells me to wait for him at the house. I don't. I go back home. I'm not at his beck and call. He can't just order me around or do whatever he wants.

None of what's happened so far prepares for me what happens next. There's no good way to prepare for a fantasy going sour. No soft way to approach the intense pain of lost childhood certainties about life. I can't even try. I'm just gonna tell you what happened.

Awkward beach incident over and purposefully pushed to the back of everyone's mind, Michella and I accept an invitation to a party at Rob's place on Chase Avenue. During his phone call, he makes it unmistakably clear he wants it to be just us. Michella, mothering soul that she is, insists on bringing friends and pushes it until he agrees to "some" friends. Not too many, and only on the condition that I will definitely be there.

We've continued to be in a spot where Rob can only contact me through my best friend, because I can't afford a cell phone and Gladys is still set on keeping her phone line hostage. Rob still hasn't bothered to talk to my parents about working together, which is creating some tension since it means he's constantly contacting Michella at her house. Her mom probably thinks *she's* got a secret boyfriend that keeps calling to chat.

Tonight, though, our excitement is palpable. A group of us from my high school are legit headed to R. Kelly's for a party. The idea alone is wild. We put effort in, so we are dressed to the *nines*. I got several of my girls with me and two good guy friends. Since we go to a wealthy school, they're all crazy-rich Jewish kids, which means we're piling into flashy cars and borrowing dresses Michella and I could never afford. We are *hyped*.

Strolling through the front doors in our fancy getups, after finding parking way down the street, it's immediately obvious this is not our regular-type house party. There are loads of women everywhere. Nothing but women and more women. As usual, Rob is nowhere to be found. Why did he invite us to this? Taking it all in is shock enough. A stripper pole flashes under lights in the middle of the main living room. Dancers are everywhere, stalking the room like cats. They lean over the right people and laugh at the right moments, sweat shining on their bodies and heels high as can be. The air itself is hot and chaotic, and the combination is suffocating.

My friends like to party, but not like this. Despite the money in their pockets, they're still average teenagers who go to football afterparties to basically drink in the basements of our parents' homes. This isn't our scene. None of us have experienced this on our own terms yet, especially with people our own age. It's over our heads. Everything is a little disjointed—no one knows where to go, where to look, who to talk to, or how to not be obviously out of place. This is next level shit and no one seems up for it. We've drank, but not shots off bare bodies. We thought we partied somewhat, until now.

Slipping under and around ladies in sparkling, sleek outfits, I start wandering and hunting for Rob while trying to avoid brushing my dress against sweaty partygoers. Instead of Rob, I run into Mack, who flashes a smile and yells loudly over the noise, "Oh hey! Rob is waiting on you!"

"Really? Because he *doesn't seem to be here*!"

"Yeah, I'm gonna call him for you."

"Mack, if he's not coming back it's fine, but we're gonna leave."

"No, no, no." He waves his hands dismissively. "No, just stay here. He'll be here."

I'm not entirely sure if he means this exact spot or the house in general, but the group agrees to hang for a bit. We stay mainly on the edges, sipping at drinks, talking amongst ourselves instead of other people, watching the crowd. Big time athletes occasionally push through to grab drinks and a couple famous names meander past, saying hi to other guests. The strippers are still everywhere, but mainly congregating around the athletes when they can manage it. We're on the verge of leaving when Mack tugs on my arm, holding the phone in his other hand.

"Rob's on for you."

I clutch the receiver hard against my ear. "We're here. You're not, and it's not really my kind of party."

"We were out," Rob's voice crackles over the phone.

"Okay. Well, right now it's just a bunch of women stripping and jumping into the pool and all that. My friends aren't really feeling it. We're about to leave."

"No, I'm gonna send for you. I'll send a car to bring you to the studio so you don't have to hang out there without me."

Glancing at my friends sheltering in the corners away from the madness, I say, "Well, let me tell my friends."

"No. Your friends can't come."

"Sorry?" I'm practically yelling it into the phone.

"I don't know them, and I don't want everyone out there knowing my business. Remember? In case you haven't noticed, I'm big, celebrity status, and I'm not gonna be around a bunch of little kids."

I pause at this. What am I then? A little kid?

"Okay." I'm uncertain how to break this to everyone else. "Let me talk to Michella for a second."

She knows it's coming just from the look on my face. "Lissie," she grumbles, "it's weird here. The whole thing feels off. We're leaving. Are you coming with us? You can't really be thinking of staying here." She's mad, I can tell. "Shit, girl. I don't even know what to say to you right now." I'm about to open my mouth when she continues anyway, "Doesn't matter. We're leaving, and I suggest you come with us."

It's impossible to hide the cringe in my voice as I mumble, "Nah, I'm gonna stay."

I can't look her in the eyes. When I finally do, hurt is flashing across her face. She adjusts her purse as she leans in close to make sure I hear. "Well don't call me tomorrow if somethin' happens." Swiveling on fancy, borrowed heels, Michella parades off with our other friends. I can see some of them peering back in confusion. I'm alone and Rob has hung up.

There's a space closer to the backside of the house that's a bit hidden away from the main festivities, another sunken living room but with less people and squishy couches. I slowly drift back there and sink into a seat, watching distantly for about an hour until Mack comes in. At first, he only wants to talk about Michella. Not surprising, since he always wants to talk to me about Michella. He's not getting any farther with her.

In the middle of telling me about their conversation tonight, he holds up the mostly full drink he's been double fisting. "Hey, you don't have a drink yet. You wanna drink?" It's some kind of punch sloshing around in a plastic cup. I gulp it down as he stands up to get himself another one. I immediately start feeling a headache coming on. When Mack returns with another drink, he's carrying a phone too. It's Rob.

"Zette, come to the studio, I want you to come to me. What are you doing right now?"

"I'm waiting, like you told me to. I thought you were sending someone to pick me up. Please, I don't want to stay here. Your cousin gave me a drink and now I have a headache and…"

"Wait, he what?" His tone is sharp.

"You told me not to go home yet, so I'm here and trying, but I just want to go."

The sigh on the other side is heavy, annoyed. Like a person swatting away a fly. "Hand the phone back to Mack." I can tell Mack doesn't want it. He swallows hard and turns his body away from me, looking nervous. Even over the blasting music, I can hear the gist of what's being said. "You can't be hittin' on my girl… underage, why you doing that to her? Giving her drinks and all." There's more but I can't make it out. Mack turns and hands me the phone with a sigh.

"That's not what I was tryin' to do, just so we're clear. Let me know if you need somethin'."

I take the phone from Mack. As I press it up to my face, there's a long exhale and I hear, "I can't talk anymore, but Big John's coming to get you. He's gonna bring you to the studio." *Click.* Is he mad I accepted the drink? It's not like Mack was hitting on me. I was alone and didn't have a drink. He was just trying to be nice while I waited for freaking Rob.

I sink back into the couch and numbly watch the girls dance, peeling off sequined bits and pieces of outfits, climbing up and leaning back on the poles as they spin. Between the colors and the constant spiraling, my stomach starts to turn. Suddenly Big John is standing in front of me, clutching an arm to help me off the couch and informing me we're headed to the studio.

By the time we arrive, the room is pretty much empty. It's just Rob and some shorter guy with a backpack who looks super young and earnest. They're focusing intently on something until I pass through the doorway and drop my purse on a chair. The new guy looks up and greets me with a warm smile.

He trots over with one hand extended out to me. "Oh, hi! I heard someone was coming. What's your name?"

"Hi. Lizzette." I squeeze his hand lightly before quickly dropping mine at my side. Earlier this evening with Mack already taught me to be cautious.

He introduces himself as K, a friend of Rob's from Chicago who is also a music artist and young producer, working on becoming one of the best rappers of his generation. Knowing Robert gets jealous easily, and aware he's in a mood tonight after overhearing his phone conversation with Mack, I keep a safe distance. Sitting farther away than usual, I pretend to not take any interest in what they're doing and seem as unphased as possible. This kid is hyped up and happy to be working with Rob, though, and clearly didn't get the memo about our tense start to the night. He pulls me into their conversation constantly and makes little, borderline-flirtatious remarks, asking if I have any sisters, things like that.

When they finally decide to wrap up, K asks if it's possible to catch a ride. Rob drives the Mercedes with just the three of us—Big John left earlier. I'm in front with Rob, and K is in back, leaning forward to talk to us. He's still being super personable, which shouldn't be an issue, but he picked the wrong night. That old saying, "You could cut the tension with a knife…" In this case, it might have required an axe. And it's still going downhill.

Rob is stoic, staring straight ahead, not really responding to the conversation much, and not taking his eyes off the road ever. He's upset with me more than anything. I'm trying to defuse it all by laughing it off, not engaging too much, and continuing to face forward or watch the passing neighborhoods.

Out of nowhere, cars start following us. Cameras flash outside the Mercedes, and I can hear shouts and tires screeching as vehicles swerve dangerously to keep up. Panic grips me as Rob seizes the back of my neck and pushes my head down to the floor of the car. He's driving with one hand and I'm doubled over, my head between my knees as he presses into it, holding me there. My short hair falls forward, tickling my cheeks.

His fingers squeeze my neck as he snaps, "I already told you, when you're with me, you don't look at anyone else. You try not to be seen." My shoulders are starting to cramp, but I stay in that position as he slowly lifts his hand back up to the wheel. It takes about ten minutes, but once we leave the paparazzi behind, I sit up, shaking. Uncertain what to do, I stare out the window. In the reflection on the glass, I can see our companion's shocked face. He keeps to himself for the rest of the drive.

We park outside this little Art Deco Hotel in South Beach where K is staying. He and Rob bump fists as he says, "Thank you, man, for all your help today." As he's closing the car door, he leans into my window. "Nice to meet you, Lizzette. And you're *sure* you don't have a sister somewhere I can take out?" My fake grin is starting to strain. I want to shout at him, *Leave me alone, you're getting me in trouble!*

Rob's glare pierces at me as K leans down into my window. He's just being friendly, but I worry Rob's upset his attention keeps including me, and the whole night is ruined. As K waves us off, shifting his backpack to one shoulder and heading towards the glass front doors, I whisper to Rob, "Okay, let's get out of here."

We only make it about a block before he starts yelling at me. "I don't know who you think you are talkin' up my friend!"

"I wasn't trying to talk to him. He was talking to *me*."

"That's your problem. You talk back too much."

Tears form as I turn to him and ask, "Why are treating me like this? I didn't do anything."

"You need to learn your place." He's not even looking at me; his eyes are fixed straight ahead again. "I told you before, you don't look at anyone and you don't look out the fuckin' window because there might be press trying to follow us. You stay down. I don't need that shit." Keeping my head tilted towards my lap this time so no one can see me if they pull up next to us, tears fall to my dress. There's no way to stop them at this point and it doesn't matter anyway. It's not even my dress. I borrowed it from a friend. A tingling runs up my leg as Rob's hand gently caresses it.

"'Ey, calm down. It's okay," he whispers to me. I let him comfort me as we drive the rest of the way back to the house.

The moment Rob sets foot inside the door of the Chase Avenue residence, a screaming cluster of women are clawing their way towards him. Excited shrieks split through the pumping music, and he's swarmed by bodies in seconds. Passing hands trail lightly on his back and across his chest, hips stretch forward to get closer, the crook of an elbow is slung around his shoulder, and fingers stretch out just enough to graze his clothes like he's going to heal them with the power of his basketball shorts.

Scanning the room to focus on anything but the groupies, it surprises me when a hand abruptly pushes under my elbow and I realize Rob is rushing me up the stairs, away from the madness. His voice rings in my ear to tell me to keep heading up, so I do. Once we're safe in his room, the master bedroom, I sink onto the bed as he strokes my arm, saying, "Just hang out in here for a while." Then he squeezes my hand once and stands up.

"Wait, where are you going? Are you leaving me?" I've spent most of the night waiting around for him, and I'm nervous about being left alone at this kind of party. My sole reassurance there is knowing Rob wouldn't stand for anyone messing with me for one second. They'd regret it forever.

He shrugs. "I need to go downstairs for a bit. It's my party. I have to show."

I'm torn between wanting to be with him and hating the crowd down there right now. The rest of the car ride had been quiet, so maybe Rob figures I'm in a mood and will ruin the party vibe. That could be why he pulled me up here so fast. Not to protect me, but to not have to look after me. Although it's also possible he might actually care, knowing I've had a rough night. Could be, because he's right there in front of me, telling me it's okay to sleep, he'll wake me up later.

Still foggy from the punch I drank earlier, I nod and relax into the sheets. Sleeping for a bit sounds nice. I can join whenever. They'll probably be going hard for a while. If I'm too tired for that, Rob will wake me up when he's ready to take me home, or we can hang out tomorrow since it's Saturday. But when Rob's muffled footsteps leave the hall, all the women start squealing again in blaring, high-pitched tones… like a celebrity just showed up to party. Even in my sleepy state it sounds like fun. Crazy fun. Maybe too much fun, so now I don't dare open the door. Not sure I want to see what's happening.

At this point, I'm tipsy, but not drunk enough to simply drift off with everything going on in the house. At the edge of my awareness, my body still pulses with tension from the car ride. I try to lose myself to sleep, but I can't. Tossing and turning, my ears naturally tune into the events downstairs. Deep down, I do want to know exactly what's going on. I don't have to try too hard to guess. Men are cheering and clapping, there's odd thumping noises, and women are hollering, sending out catcalls and whistles. From the sound of it, and the sudden bursts of noise, Rob is giving a show. Or getting one. Maybe dancing... possibly stripping, but now is not the time to think about that. Ugh, now he *must* be taking clothes off... the racket just got intense and wild.

Stepping gingerly over to the door, despite the ruckus (it's not like anyone could have heard me anyway), I crack it a smidge and try to catch a glimpse of what's happening. The angle is wrong from my post at the door, though, so I can't see much. Too many women are crowding around him, blocking my view.

I want to go home. I want to run out the door and keep running until I pass through the front door and fall into the safety of my own bed. Michella already left. My friends split too, went to a club when they didn't like the vibe here. I'm stuck. Unless I'm ready to sprint past everyone, into the street, and attempt to find my way home, or better yet, call my parents by waking up Gladys. Ha, no. I got nothing. *Stuck.* The word sinks into my chest, burning as if I drank something hot too quickly. Nudging the door shut, I head back to the bed, wrap myself up, and try once more to force myself to rest. My consciousness finally manages to drift into a light, stressful sleep.

Early morning rays fight through the blinds when Rob finally knocks the door open hours later. Crawling onto the bed, I can feel his hands on my body, running up and down, gripping a hip, squeezing my thigh. His fingers start moving faster, squeezing harder, and the movements became more intense, more frantic.

"Take off your clothes," I hear in my ear.

"What?" The fog is still there.

Not waiting any longer, Rob grabs me by the waist and flips me onto my back, kissing me roughly. He reaches one arm across my shoulder and pushes himself over me, fingers first fiddling with my pants then pulling at them, sliding them down and off my ankles. I'm stuck between frozen uncertainty and searching for some kind of absent self-preservation instinct about what I should do. My brain offers me nothing. I stay frozen. My head still aches from the spiked drink. I've hardly slept, and my mind goes numb at the harsh touch.

What is he doing? As he hooks a thumb around the edge of my underwear, my hips lift automatically to help. It feels like what I'm supposed to do. What I *have* to do. What am I doing, again?

Rob strips down quickly, his undressing taking only seconds because his daily outfit is always gym shorts and a Nike shirt. No undergarments. Ever. The only part that takes any time at all is him yanking the glorified Nike Jordans off his feet. Then he kisses me hard again and rolls me back onto my side, holding me close from behind, hands running and reaching everywhere. I can feel him sliding between my legs, poking, pausing, then forcing up and in as pain tears through me.

I'm a virgin. Or I was. He never asked me directly, but he knew. Or if he didn't know before, he does now. I thought this moment normally came with candles, maybe dinner, sweet caresses under the moonlight?

Thoughts circle in slow motion, drifting just out of reach, like I'm not all the way here. I'm not on birth control and don't carry condoms because I've never needed to. *Wait!* I'm screaming inside my head. *I'm not prepared for this.* What do I do if I get pregnant? It hurts so much and I don't think he's noticed. Do I say something? Rob pulls away and I can sense him readjusting. He's resting back on bent knees and for a moment I think it's over. Then he maneuvers my hips to flip me over and prop me on all fours.

Holding me up with one hand, each cycle burns with fresh pain. Eyes watery, I turn my head to try and look into his eyes, blinking away tears, but it's like he isn't really there. His eyes are unfocused, just staring, almost angry looking. Someone is there, but the Rob I know is definitely not. He hardly notices me. The intensity on his face says, *This is what I'm doing right now, and it's what it's gonna be.*

There aren't other options. Any thought I had of stopping him disappears. I'm afraid of that face. All he's tuned into is the motion—himself in me, what *he's* doing. I'm struggling to stay up on hands and knees for him, wanting to prove I'm capable, his equal, but it hurts so much. This is what it's like though, right? He wants me. And this is what he wants from me right now.

Next thing I know he's tugging at my arm, pushing me to the ground until I'm on my knees. I've heard about what happens here but have never done this before either. I'm nervous. Does it hurt? Is it possible to do it wrong? I quickly realize it doesn't matter. He's directing everything.

"Move this way."

"Oh yeah, baby, do that."

"No, stretch your leg like this."

"Mm, get over here."

"Now spit on it. Yes, like that, babe."

I'm choking on him. He doesn't wait for me to try and figure it out. His hands push my head towards him as I try not to gag. I catch a breath whenever he pulls out, slapping it on my face. Fingers grip the back of my head, tense in my hair. As he doubles over, it comes into my mouth, but he's still gripping so I can't pull away. I want to throw up. With one last slide of his hand to release the last of it, he lets me go and collapses back onto the bed with a deep sigh.

Still on my knees on the floor, I'm trying not to vomit. Wiping my mouth with the back of my hand, I crawl back onto the bed and lay there, tears streaming, knees tucked up to my chest. The lower part of my body burns with hot pain.

Rob doesn't touch me. At some point, his weight shifts off the bed and I hear him pull his clothes back on before the door clicks open and then shut. Everything is throbbing. If I keep still enough, maybe it'll go away. From the distant buzz of blended sounds, there's clearly still a party, but it's not poppin' the way it was before. Voices, laughter, and heavy bass reverberate through the walls, but it's died down some.

It seems like no time at all has passed when Rob swings the door open again and heads into the bathroom. It sounds like he's sniffling. I can't imagine he's crying in there; I must be hearing it wrong.

Suddenly, Rob is out on the carpet in front of me leaping around in a decorative tribal mask he plucked off the wall. He is fucking wired and dancing like a crazy person. Meanwhile I'm miserably crying on the bed, limply watching from a pillow soaked with tears. Maybe he's trying to break the ice by being ridiculous. It doesn't take a genius to know I'm hurting. He probably doesn't know how to make me feel better.

When I don't muster much of a response, he sets the mask in the bathroom and disappears downstairs again. I continue to lay there, heart thumping, my legs pressed tight together as I lie on my side and stare at the wall. When the door clicks again, it's Rob shutting it behind himself before stretching out on the bed to sleep.

When his breathing becomes relaxed and heavy, and I'm positive he's asleep, I pull on clothes, creep downstairs and clean up the party wreckage. Everyone else is, thankfully, shut into rooms, gone home, or sleeping the night off wherever they found a spot. My only companion is Twelve Play the pug, who adores me and follows me around as I pick up the entire downstairs area. It is *trashed*. Never seen anything like it. The idea of going back upstairs, though, seems impossible. I feel dirty and damaged and all I want is to feel clean. Also, I'm Puerto Rican and I was hardcore trained to be helpful to any and all hosts. You don't lose that instinct even when you're coming unglued. Right now, it's giving me a distraction and I need it.

So, in shock, I clean the kitchen. I tidy the little piece of the world I have control over. Twelve Play scampers around my feet as my solace as I collect empty bottles, scrub counters, and sweep floors. Maybe he can tell I'm hurting. I feel different, and not in a good way.

As I'm finishing up, Rob traipses down the stairs. In response, I head back upstairs. His friends are starting to get up and I don't want to see them. I don't want them to see me. I feel like everyone will be able to tell, like everyone knows already what happened last night.

I'm surprised to see Rob back in the room in no time clutching my black mini backpack. Between ringed fingers, he holds up my school photo from when my hair was still long. Guess he went through my stuff… and looked through my planner while he was carrying it up to the room.

"Why'd you cut your hair?"

Not the words I was expecting. "Sorry, what?" Of all things to bring up right now.

"Your hair. Why'd you cut it? You looked so much better with long hair."

I can't keep my mouth from dropping open. No "thanks for cleaning the house," no mention of anything that happened last night, no concern for how I'm feeling, just crappin' on my hairstyle.

"Don't leave your bag down there, there are thieves in this house," he says, and throws the bag at me. Fighting back tears, I rest my backpack next to the bed, curl onto my side, and pull a blanket over my head. I don't have a toothbrush, I don't have fresh clothes, nothing to get ready if I take a bath or shower. It's okay, I guess. Deep down, I know I don't have energy for that anyway. It's like my strength also disappeared behind the blocked-off wall of my emotions. All my energy sapped and sucked up into the paralyzing hurricane of thoughts spent trying to make sense of the last night.

Everything from here on is fuzzy and doesn't seem quite real. Pretty sure he invites me to the studio, but I have nothing to get ready with or wear. I hear him say he'll buy me some stuff or maybe send Big John back with some things for me.

Then he leaves and I lay there, unmoving, the entire rest of the day.

At least my mom won't worry this time. Planning ahead for a fun weekend, I already told her I'd be at Michella's place until Sunday night. Laying there in the semi-darkness under the blanket reminds me over and over that I'm feeling alone and sad and helpless. Can't help it. It all just keeps swirling through my head.

Rob never comes back. I stay in bed the whole night, curled in on myself, wishing I kept a toothbrush in my purse.

Sunday morning, he's there when I wake up. Expecting some kind of explanation, tenderness, anything, I sit up and turn towards him, waiting. He hands me forty dollars to take a cab home. I'm dismissed.

I don't go home. I direct the driver to Michella's house, then lay in bed there and cry. I don't see Robert again for weeks.

CHAPTER 9

The first time I was sexually assaulted I was six years old. We lived in Borough Park in Brooklyn, New York, in a one-bedroom apartment. Mom slept on the pull-out sofa in the living room, in front of the television. I had my own private room. My mother's boyfriend owned a local arcade and stayed over often. It wasn't unusual to find him at the kitchen table drinking coffee when I dragged myself to a kitchen chair for breakfast in the morning.

Early one Saturday, Mom was brewing coffee and realized we had run out of sugar. A shout from the kitchen explained she was going to the neighbor's house to grab some. At this, I poked my head out of my room and wandered out into the hallway, just catching sight of her coat-sleeve as she closed the door behind her. Only then did I notice Mr. Boyfriend, who leaned shirtless against the arm of the sofa. Watching me linger at the edge of the kitchen, he patted the open mattress space next to him, telling me to come take a seat.

Once settled on the sofa bed beside him, legs crisscrossed, his large hand folded around mine. He massaged it for a second before unzipping his pants and using it on himself, eyes focused on me. Then, pushing at my shoulder, he had me lie down and put himself on my lips, telling me to open my mouth. I shook my head, lips pressed tight, so he told me to open my mouth like a good girl should. If I didn't, he said, he would hurt my mom. Complying, I opened my small mouth, struggling to breathe in the short fragment of time before the front doorknob began to twist. The noise startled both of us, and as he pulled away in a rush, wrestling with the button of his jeans, I jumped off the bed and ran into my room. Slamming it behind me, I leapt into the safety of my bed and stayed there.

My mother must have noticed something was off, because she knocked soon after and perched at the end of the bed, asking if I was okay. Guessing what she would want me to say, what would make her feel better, I said yes. A few days later I came home from school to Mom cracking open what looked like a third or fourth beer and cooking eggs and rice with sausage. A usual of ours, I headed straight to the fridge to pull out the ketchup and set it next to my plate on the table.

She knelt down beside me as I shifted a hip onto my chair. "Baby, did something happen when I was getting sugar the other day?" I didn't want to answer. I knew it was bad and I didn't know how this would go or if I would be in trouble. "Please, tell me. It's really important that you tell me, Lissie." The second I said yes, she started sobbing, followed by yelling at the empty air and pacing the floor while rubbing at her face. Then she got on the phone.

The phone call was to my Uncle Ephraim, her younger brother and a notorious street boxer. Known for being tough—no games played—he was my absolute favorite uncle. Fit and strong as can be, but also carrying a huge soft spot for his family. He had a good heart, everyone could tell.

A few days later the arcade was gone, destroyed in a fire, and the owner was nowhere to be found. I wondered if it was my fault.

***

Same as when I was a kid, I don't bring anything up. I would lose everything that matters to me right now if I lost Rob. He knows he hurt me—he watched me cry, saw the pain, he's aware. It's still nagging at me that he hasn't apologized or mentioned it. So now, I listen to sad music and try to justify it to myself.

He cares about you, and you were practically together anyway. You knew it was going to happen at some point. You put yourself in that position. It's not just on him. Maybe he was drunk or the drugs messed with him so he didn't have his head straight either. He's had it rough too. We're both hurting. It's good we found each other in all this mess.

After what point is numbness the basis of where you start every relationship and every sexual encounter? When you're abused as a child, where do you learn the lines of what's normal and what's not? Why is there no book that lists all the ground rules? Your fairy godmother should be coming in a puff of smoke. Peter Pan arriving at your window to take you away before you grow up too fast. Even when stuff hurt, or felt entirely wrong, everything set up around it made it feel normal, almost expected. This is life. You accept it.

The second time I was handled inappropriately, it was my older male cousin. The third, my babysitting gig. He told me to take my things off because he wanted me to try on his wife's clothes so he could see what fit and then would maybe consider giving me some items.

The good parts with Rob were fairytale unreal. Even looking back, some days were like a dream out of nowhere. Attending classes before being picked up by bodyguards in spotless cars, spending the afternoons with Robert, hanging out in some of the best studios in the country while watching a world talent create music… beyond surreal. And people noticed the change in me. I finally felt loved. I wore the presents, I skipped classes to be with him, and I made a million excuses in my head for why I should stick around despite that we weren't making music together and he could be incredibly demeaning.

The optimism and hope for the promised future music career kept drifting just out of reach in front of me, like catching a page of sheet music blowing in the wind. Something was always preventing, not ready, or in the way. I wanted to so badly to believe everything was where it started that I chose to believe it, regardless.

***

On a sunny Monday after school, I tell my mom I'm spending the evening with Michella and it'll run late. Michella shows up to my house in Miriam's little broken-down car. Miriam is her mom's partner. We don't ask for permission; we've been taking it for years while they pass out together. They're happy drunks, celebrating life in the moment and forgetting about the world—best way to do it. So we don't feel too bad about making our own lives and cutting a corner here or there.

We look up the new address Rob gave us earlier—because it's a separate rental house—and I guide while my girl drives. Windows stay shut so we don't mess up our hair. We glance at each other and crack up. We're two teenagers on the way to one of R. Kelly's houses, *again*.

I'm expecting something like the place we've already been, since they're both rentals. Nothing fancy or anything. Oh, hell no. It's right next to Julio Iglesias's house. It's at like 55th and North Bay Road. *Mansion Road* is what they call it. Madonna has a house here somewhere. All the celebrities live in this neighborhood. Everything is gated and expansive, grassy estates with long winding driveways which are basically paved hills. We pull along a curb and park in front of a huge mansion. You can hear party noises all the way from outside the decorative closed gate at the end of the driveway.

Shit, the gate is closed. How are we gonna get in? We park and walk up to the gate to see if it's unlocked. Nope, no such luck. That's strange; Rob knows I'm coming. We don't have cell phones yet, so it's either turn around and go home or find a way in. So… we jump the gate.

We try to be subtle. It's hard in heels and a skirt. Plus, this is a posh neighborhood, so if we look like we're breaking in, the cops will be called in a *heartbeat* and we will be in jail. There's always nosy people watching areas like this with all the high-priced cars parked everywhere. I've never done anything like gate-jumping before, but what are we supposed to do? Leave? Rob is expecting me, and I didn't come before like he wanted.

The cheers and whistles of a football game drift through the closed front door, which is left unlocked. Inside, a number of people are talking and watching the game with beers in hand. The interior is impressive, but Rob isn't here.

"Maybe we should call him?" Michella shrugs and points at a phone on a nearby side table. Agreeing it would be silly to give up and leave now, I pick it up, dial, and listen to it ring until he picks up.

"Hello?"

"Hey! Why didn't you leave the gate open?"

"Zette? Whaddya mean the gate's closed? I told them to leave it open! Promise. I had to come down to the studio for a bit. Oh my god, I swear I told them."

"Okay." I'm glad no one else can hear me with all the background noise, but I cup my hand over the mouthpiece anyway. "I just jumped over it to get in."

Rob clearly thinks this is the funniest shit he's ever heard. "Are you serious?" Laughter roars out of the earpiece and I hold the phone further from my ear. It takes him a bit to calm down.

"What was I supposed to do?" I'm annoyed. "We live far away. We're not going to turn around and head back just to call you and drive here again. We don't have money for that kind of gas. Our other option was going home and staying home."

When he finally catches his breath, he responds, "That's the cutest shit I've heard in a while. You can go up to my room if you want and just chill upstairs. I won't be there for an hour or two, but you can watch TV or whatever until I get there."

On the way to the master bedroom, Michella and I inspect the place a bit. Not trying to snoop or anything—maybe we are. The house is so freakin' giant, right on the intercoastal waterway, with a yacht in the back, and seven bedrooms. Deep voices spill out of one room, which turns out to be full of men all crowded in, chatting loudly, interrupting each other, and having a good time. We keep climbing stairs, searching for Rob's room. He told us where it is, but the house is so big.

A tad more wandering and I'm pushing open the door to Rob's private living space, the master bedroom. Michella and I slink in awkwardly. It is a little weird to be in someone's room without them when you've never visited before *with* them. My feet stop before I'm even entirely inside and Michella bumps into my shoulder, then looks over it, following my gaze. Women's clothing is strewn all over. Makeup bags, eyeliner pencils, blush, mascara, straighteners, and curling irons pile up in random places and lay stacked in front of mirrors. Heels of various bright colors and heights lay scattered everywhere.

"What the hell." Michella's voice cracks through the panicked ringing in my ears. I know I'm not Rob's girlfriend, obviously, but we've been intimate, close. Instead of rage, I can only muster disappointment and a sense of dread. I don't know where I am on the list. Didn't know there was a list. It felt like we were getting there, like he wanted me to be a permanent fixture in his life. I love him. We've said it already. Both of us.

Yet here is the evidence of other women dumped across the floor. The reality of others isn't quite kicking in. It doesn't fit. *He told me he loved me.*

As the hurt ripples out from unbreathing lungs, anger swells and I start to cry. Michella looks at me. "Girl, why you crying?"

"I mean, look at this!" I wave my hand at the messy fragments of other people's lives. Other women's lives.

"Well," she says slowly, "What did you think he was doing? You think there's no other girls?"

Despite Michella's advice, I call him on the house phone. I'm shouting from the second he picks up. "What the hell is wrong with you!? Why would you even tell me to come here? What if a girl was staying in your room when I got here? Why would you do this? Are you trying to intentionally hurt me?" I'm flinging questions as fast as they can race through my head and out my mouth.

Rob's curses pound through the phone back at me, followed by, "You really think that? That's your problem!" I start to lose my courage entirely. Maybe it is my problem. "You're just jumping to conclusions because you saw something you don't get."

"You told me to go to your room." Don't let my voice shake. Focus on that. "That's *your* room. So you know, me with my friend here too… it's embarrassing. I feel stupid here."

"Okay? Well, that isn't my fault. That isn't my girl stuff 'cause, you know, I wouldn't do that to you, and I don't have other girls I'm bringing to the house." Rob goes on to tell me his female friend has been staying there while he's in the studio and moving around to different places. Switching to smooth and consoling, he claims none of that stuff is his or has anything to do with him. Maybe it's true. Probably not, but I want to believe him. Still angry, he hangs up on me.

Michella shrugs and asks me, "Do you have to stay here and wait for him? 'Cause, sorry, but I gotta go." With a silent nod, I let her leave. I'm not sure if I believe Rob, but I give in. I wait.

He shows up late, late, *late*. My mom is probably waiting for my call, but I'm at the point where I don't care anymore. It doesn't matter if I go home or what she says. My anxiety is high already. Rob explaining this situation to my face is more important to me than reassuring my mom right now. He shows up in the middle of the night, but *his* version of 'middle of the night.' Super fucking late.

Since I stayed, he's sweet when he gets back. We watch TV, talking and laughing through it, his arm around me, until he puts his hand on the back of my head and starts pushing it down towards his lap. I've never initiated this movement from this direction, so I don't really know what to do. My eyes are watering and I feel stupid all over again. I sneak a look up at him so he can see I don't like it. Instead, he gets mad. "I'm gonna have to teach you everything 'cause you don't know." Then he coaches me his way, what he likes. I do it exactly the way he says.

Sleep eludes me after that. I roll back and forth, trying to get comfortable, but my heart is racing. I'm anxious he's going to start again, need me to do it again, and I won't be ready. Lying still as can be, I wait for his fingers to start seeking me out again, dreading it. I want to be left alone for the rest of the night. As the sun starts coming up and glinting through the curtains, he sits up and turns to me. My panic is immediate, and my heart begins to race.

"Let's go sleep in the closet."

"What?"

"Too many windows in this room," he says as he grabs blankets and trudges off. I follow, clutching pillows and a quilt. We sleep the rest of the morning in the darkness of the closet. Somehow it feels safer in that enclosed space, wrapped up in a cocoon of blankets. When we wake hours later, I take one peek in the mirror and almost laugh. I look a mess.

"I have to iron my clothes before I go home." I hold up the wrinkled garments so he can see how bad they are. "Like now, before I get dressed. They look terrible."

"Don't worry, I'm gonna take you shopping for some new ones." His big grin makes me smile in return. I guess it's his way of apologizing. Finally. "Go take a shower, Zette, get yourself ready, whatever you need." Letting the shower run over me, I feel surprisingly calm, like last night's discomfort didn't happen. Holding the clothes up to myself in the bathroom entryway, I remind Rob that I still need that iron. To my surprise, he immediately goes downstairs, comes back up with an iron, and cheerfully irons my clothes for me. He's smiling at me, offering to grab things for me, asking if I need anything, kissing me on the cheek. It's disconcerting, but hell, I'm going to enjoy it. If this is his way of getting back into good graces, I'm not sad about it. He's treating me like a queen.

True to his word, Rob takes me to the mall to buy some new clothes. We're accompanied by his friends (as usual), and instead of guiding me around or escorting me into shops while I try things on, he simply hands me three hundred dollars with a wide smile.

I've never seen money like that, so it takes me a second to allow myself to pull my hand back with all of it. This is a crazy amount of money to me. As I realize he's just handing off the bills so I can do my own thing, my delight drops. I'm happy for the chance to buy new clothes and feel decent, but it feels like he's paying me off instead of talking to me about anything. Like his niceness should cover any qualms or bad feelings. It's like putting on a nice act instead of being genuine, because the truth is too hard. What about when there are bigger problems in the future? Will he just pay me off then too?

CHAPTER 10

It's late February, and a group of us are gathered at the local Bennigan's, one of Rob's usual dine-in favorites. Everyone is in good spirits—cracking jokes, talking about the new music coming out, spittin' out ridiculously tall tales about their love lives and the women who keep 'em warm at night.

I generally keep to myself, so I sit quietly and watch Rob interact. Clearly the ringleader, he's like a cyclone that keeps pulling everyone in so powerfully, you can't help but watch him. And everyone is happy just to be part of it.

During a lull in the conversation, Rob's trainer catches my eye and makes a funny comment about performance fitness to try and make me laugh. I can't help it; I bust out giggling. The others at the table chuckle and whoop until they see the solemn, angry face. Rob stands up and jerks his head towards the door, looking directly at me. "Let's go outside. Now."

Tentatively, I scootch my chair out and stand to follow him. It's already maybe 9 p.m. at night, so it's darker outside, and there aren't really people around anymore. Instead of turning to talk to me on the sidewalk out front, he leads me through the mainly empty parking lot, behind the restaurant.

"I told you I don't like it when you look at or talk to my friends." His voice is severe. "You're only supposed to look at *me*."

"But I…"

Smack. Directly across my cheek, hard enough to twist my body to the side. My shaking fingertips lightly touch my cheek, the skin burning hot underneath. My eyes well up with tears which spill over quickly, stinging as they run over tender skin.

"You need to act like a grown woman and listen to me." There's a roaring in my ears as he's speaking, it's like he's yelling from far away. "You are only supposed to look at me. Now, let's go back inside. And fix your face." He turns and heads off towards the front entrance again. I follow on trembling legs, trying to blink away the last of the tears and swipe at my makeup before it can drizzle down to my chin. Back inside and seated, I duck my head down to rummage through my purse. Shakily holding up a compact, I check my face in the tiny mirror.

Rob stares at me, straight faced, then looks around the table and says, "Women shouldn't put makeup on at the dinner table. 'S not right."

Silence lays heavy as soon as the words are out. A few people look angry, but no one says anything. I excuse myself to the bathroom to fix my makeup. I know they can see the red.

As we leave, everyone gets up one by one, moving in different directions at different times, so no one ends up paying the bill. Again. Driving home in the Landcruiser, everyone has a good laugh about it. I stay silent, clutching my purse on my lap as I watch the neighborhoods go by.

Back at Rob's place, I avoid eye contact with anyone else, keeping my distance until I end up falling asleep on a sofa. When I wake up, everyone is gone, minus one guy named Steve who is Rob's lead sound engineer. He offers me a ride home.

As I'm stepping out onto my own driveway, he puts a hand on my wrist to stop me and says, "You seem like a nice girl." I look back and give him a weak smile. "You shouldn't hang out with him."

I stay quiet and push myself out of the car.

At this point, my "real" life at home feels like a distraction from where I could be and what I could be doing with Rob's help and influence. It's almost frustrating to return at the end of the night to a place where it feels like I don't matter. All the opportunities for something better only seem substantial around Robert. It's as though my two lives swapped, and now this afterschool life feels more genuine, more real to me.

The next time I see him, it's back at the house on North Bay Road—house, mansion, whatever—which has a bell tower on top with a cubby-like space to sit. You have to take a spiral, metal staircase from the top floor to get up there, but I haven't been up yet.

When I find Rob in his room, he suggests showing me the tower, saying the bell up close is pretty cool. His grin is telling me otherwise, that it's not really about the bell, but I hear myself respond with, "I guess... let's go." Nerves tighten with each ringing step up. I've seen this look before. It means he has plans.

As I suspected, he wants me to go down on him—his favorite pastime. I hate it and basically just do it to make him happy. Also to prevent him from getting angry and keep him from giving up on someone as young and inexperienced as me. I always feel the need to prove myself.

I cringe every time he calls me "head champ." It's never felt like a compliment. When I asked him not to use the nickname, he said it was sexy and he's teaching me to appreciate things.

This time he switches it up after a minute or two, saying he's going to do the same for me. This is new. What do I do now? Like do I move my legs out or what? Bent knees... straight knees? Sensing my discomfort, he tells me he's never done this to a woman before, that it's new to him too. I don't believe him for a second, but I keep my mouth shut. He lays on his back and tells me to sit on him.

"Like... your chest or your face?"

He guides me down. The only thing I feel is cheap. I don't know where to look or put my hands. Most of our sexual experiences make me feel cheap, almost like I work for him. I might as well be an actress instead of a singer—told where to go, what to do, how to enjoy it, what's supposed to feel good, what I'm doing wrong. I know they're part of the balance of our relationship, but as the orders continue and grow, taking new shapes, shame at feeling like his sex toy has started turning into a deep sadness. Whenever I lose my cover and let it show, it makes him upset, and he pushes harder.

My thoughts are interrupted by his voice, loud in my ear: "Wait, don't move! Let me take a pic. Yes, Zette!" How did I get here??? This ain't a music career. We haven't even worked on my record lately. Just his. We play around in the studio. I listen to his beats and offer my thoughts when he asks. Rob is aiming for his own label, Rockland Records, and keeps saying that when it comes out, he'll make me an artist. I believe him, but it's starting to feel like it's never going to happen. Depression has been seeping in lately and filling up my chest with a heaviness like lead where I can't breathe.

Spent and sleepy, he walks me down to his room for a nap, but within the hour he's up and shaking me awake, telling me we have to go to the studio because he has to finish this one song right now and wants me to hear it. Inspired by our bell tower time, no doubt. Drowsy, but trying to be up for anything, I pull on clothes and follow him to the car for a drive to the Marlin Hotel. It's one of his favorite working spaces. Once inside, he directs me to a sofa, where I plop down in exhaustion. He clicks the mic so I can hear him with the live room acoustics from the sofa and enters the booth itself. Then he starts to sing.

"What's up baby... I know what you're thinking..."

Currently thinking about how nice either coffee or sleep sounds.

"Don't be afraid," his voice is gentle, "just let this love groove in." I smile at this. Sounds like when he's reassuring me about something new he wants to try in the bedroom. "Rules that are so very simple..." My stomach sinks and hardens. I've always thought of his quirks more as preferences, but now, hearing this said out loud, I realize they do stand as rules. If I don't follow them, there are consequences.

"...tell Daddy... what it is you want." Everything about this song is sexual. One person in charge, taking the other along. It's seductive, but it's making me uneasy. "Let me take you to a place..." This sounds more like rape than a love track. He taps on the glass at me as he says, "Couldn't sleep with all this on my mind, after our time together earlier."

The knot in my stomach is starting to hurt. Is it a reminder that he's the one in charge or is he actually trying to be sweet? I want to run and hide in the bathroom, process it alone, but I'm glued to the couch. It's amazing how he can be so charming, then in the same breath, make me feel disgusting and powerless, like I'm just here to bend to his will. Being with R. Kelly is not the same as being with Robert. Whichever I get at any given time, he still holds all the cards, and he knows it.

CHAPTER 11

The tension between my mother and I keeps getting worse, and our relationship ends up in hot water. It's started feeling like she and my stepdad gang up on me because they can, and my resentment at the two of them is getting hard to hold in. When he's upset, she sides with him, regardless of the circumstances. Always his word over mine. Generally, she doesn't even ask for my side, just wants me to submit to his rules. It feels like my entire life is subject to everyone else's rules, goals, and preferences.

Rob's houses, the studios, and the silly corporate restaurants, all of these become a refuge for me from my home life. I try talking to him about it, but it doesn't go the direction I thought it would.

"Zette," Rob tells me, "You need to understand that when you sleep with somebody, no one else can get in between that closeness. Like what your mom and your stepfather have because they sleep together, you can't get mad at them for it, and you can't expect them to go against each other for you."

"But I'm her daughter. Blood related."

"Nobody comes between the couple. Not friends, not kids, no one."

***

Rob leaves for Chicago again in early March. With him gone, I'm at Michella's far too much with nothing to do. We need money to go places and we don't have it, so we expand beyond our clothing business.

There's an eighteen-and-over club on South Beach called Cameo Nightclub. Michella makes friends with everybody everywhere she goes, and this includes the Cameo front door guy. Licenses and IDs are always laminated, so you can change the date with a safety pin and an eraser… or so Michella discovers. Pretty much everyone besides her is still seventeen, so she adjusts everyone else's, for a price. On top of that income, she and the door guy are in together too, charging extra at the door since he knows they're underage. Then they split the proceeds. This isn't five friends or something, it's most of our school, so it's a pretty lucrative short-term deal.

Michella helps ensure business, so tonight there'll be a large group of us arriving at the same time, ready to celebrate. The bouncer collects $40 a head to let people in our group skip the line and go straight inside. She takes twenty, and the bouncer keeps twenty. Everyone else is thrilled just to feel special and make it inside without issues.

Normally, I'm not a drinker. It's not my style and I weigh maybe 105 pounds with my thickest heels on, but tonight, I decide to drink. Between avoiding my own home and not hearing from Rob whatsoever lately, I'm feeling a little depressed. He says he's in Chicago, but really, who knows.

Remember that whole I-don't-really-drink-and-weigh-almost-nothing aspect? Well, my friends decide to sign me up for a dance-off onstage. Me undertaking a dance-off requires much more alcohol than a drink or two. The combination of underweight and barely any tolerance hits me hard. It doesn't take a lot to drink way too much and stumble through the dance portion. Thankfully, it's time to go almost as soon as I'm off the stage. Emphasis on the "go" because I barely make it outside before I start vomiting someone's mom's spaghetti on the street, half a leg already in the car. Everyone else is already buckled in, watching my party demise.

"Oh my god, look! There's Rob!" Michella shouts. Frantic, I swivel my head around. There's no way. He hasn't called and he's supposed to be in Chicago. But sure enough, his black Toyota Landcruiser with the 12PLAY license plate is right behind the car I'm sticking out of. Mortified, I tuck myself in through the door as fast as possible so we can leave. My face is burning with heat, but the shame transforms into anger in no time. He couldn't even call, doesn't tell me he's here, but he was right here the whole time. For how long, though? It's like the beach scenario all over again. If he was keeping an eye on me... I race back through memories, trying to determine if there's anything I'd regret him seeing, anything that might be brought up later. I shouldn't be worried about his feelings when he's spying on me, but now I'm wary of accidentally upsetting him even when he's not around.

Soon enough, I learn to assume that I'm under Rob's watch pretty much all the time. If it isn't him personally, he sends someone. He likes to check in to make sure I'm loyal but doesn't generally extend it to making sure I'm okay. An odd conundrum.

Despite the intensity of constant scrutinization, there's an aspect to it that's uplifting. He cares. So I do what I can to help him trust me. If Rob doesn't like someone, other than Michella, I stop hanging out with them. It's simple. And it's not like it's anyone I was super close to anyway. Getting out of this shitty housing situation, out of part-time retail jobs, out of all of this, he's the person who makes me feel like I can.

I do, possibly, get slightly caught up in it all and end up in the studio or staying overnight on school days. Doesn't seem like it matters much anyway at this point. Eventually, between late arrivals and missed classes, one of my teachers calls my mom, saying my presence and efforts have been notably missing. Everything between us that's already been hovering over thin ice gives in. She kicks me out. I find my things tied up in trash bags out on the yard. We don't even exchange words at this point.

Instead, Michella insists to her moms they take me in. Michella's loved me more than anyone else my entire life. School is nearly over, so it's not forever, just a couple months. There's pushback, but she refuses to back down, insisting they let me stay with them. This does not come without repercussions.

Rob calls a few times from Chicago, or wherever he is, asking me what I'm doing. He's been talking about bringing me to the city for my birthday when I turn eighteen. It's to the point of obsession, like all he can talk about sometimes. Probably because he feels like he can't bring me before I'm technically a legal adult. Just in case.

Weirdly enough, as my eighteenth birthday gets close in mid-April, I hear nothing. The calls stop coming and I stop waiting for them. I also quit expecting a trip to Chicago. Instead, Michella and I continue low-key stealing clothes and selling 'em to make money, so we can buy ourselves plane tickets to Jacksonville to have our own celebration in style. Our friend Nicole goes to college there, so we plan on taking a plane like rich girls and heading out to the clubs.

I don't invite Rob to Jacksonville—already know he wouldn't come—but I do try calling to let him know I won't be in Miami. He gave me a cell phone to get ahold of him. One of those giant block things you can drop off a rollercoaster and it's somehow not even nicked. Nobody else knows about it really, and I don't use it to contact people generally. It was intended so I could get ahold of him and vice versa, sidestepping Gladys. I was relieved to know she wasn't listening in on phone conversations as gossip fodder for bingo club anymore.

Since I'm staying at Michella's house now, it's absolutely preferable to contact Rob directly with the cell phone. No way I'm running up a Chicago phone bill there.

Despite the ease of contact and all the promises to show me around Chicago, he never even calls to wish me a happy birthday. Like the actual date of my birthday... nothing. Don't hear from him at all. Officially an adult and officially crushed. He couldn't even take the time to push some buttons on his phone and say hello. Heartbroken me parties it off in Jacksonville to forget about both the situation and, hopefully, him.

Within a few days of this attempt to let go again, naturally, Rob calls from Chicago, concerned. Not about missing my birthday, but what I might have done after turning eighteen.

"You didn't get no tattoos, right? Zette, right?" He already told me he doesn't want me to have tattoos. Once he goes through the list of might-have-done worries, he brings up visiting him again. This time he seems serious. Over the next week, he sets everything up for the flight and my time out there. I start getting things together, and then he changes his mind.

So I'm not going to Chicago, he didn't show up for my birthday, and to top it off, my principal calls me to the office a few days later to tell me my mom came by to pay for my cap and gown, which is when they informed her I wouldn't be walking with my class. My stomach turns. This is the one thing she wanted for me, to get out of this kind of life. I know she's devastated. She doesn't even need to tell me. I hate myself for not trying harder.

Despite not technically graduating, I'm still a senior and can attend my senior prom. Rob calls directly after I leave a lowkey message about it. Priorities.

"Who you going with?"

"A group."

"Good. What you wearing?"

"A dress, Robert. Like everyone else."

"Just asking. Imma bring you to Chicago if I can't get back soon. Okay?"

"Sure. I'm excited." I don't believe him for a second, but it's easier this way.

"Be sure to take some photos at your prom, and don't drink. It doesn't lead anywhere good."

"Okay, Rob."

I pick out a gorgeous ivory dress, and my mom calls Michella's place, saying she wants to do my hair. It's tradition between us for her to style it on special occasions. She and my stepdad pick me up in a white station wagon, and we head to the dollar store to grab bobby pins for an updo.

The few times I do get to see my mother, she tends to ask super personal questions about what I've been doing with my life. This session is especially rough since she's demanding an explanation as to why I'm not graduating. She brings it up again after picking out hairpins, when we're on the way back to the house, and I tell her I don't want to talk about anything like that today, just enjoy the time we have together. Plus, I hate having these sorts of conversations in my stepdad's presence. He always makes it worse.

We're close to home, but not quite there when my stepdad reacts, "Don't speak to your mom like that, you whore." Pulling the car over to the side of the road, he shuffles it into park and swings his door wide open before circling around to my side. Tearing open my passenger door, he yanks me out with one hand around my arm. I'm still clutching the bobby pins tight. My mom ignores me as I smack the window with my free hand, screaming that we're supposed to be together today. It's important. Her cold features convince me to stop, and I lean against her window, crying. Meanwhile, my stepdad returns to the driver's seat, slams the door, and drives off, running over my left foot and leaving me on a random side street.

CHAPTER 12

While I can't dance at prom, it's still fun. After some time at the event itself, our whole group leaves the venue anyway to go to Roney Palace across from The W South Beach Hotel. Someone's parents paid for the penthouse. Probably a mistake on their part, but we're having a blast. Everyone is taking shots of something bright green, looks almost fluorescent in the light. Some kinda shit from New Orleans. I'm watching kids slam it and throw up everywhere. I told Rob I wouldn't drink, but since I can't dance either, I might as well join in on fun of some kind.

I decide to just have one. Maybe two, if I like it. I knock back a generous pour that burns my throat and makes my stomach twist as it hits. Shit. I did promise Rob I wouldn't drink. What if he has someone here watching and I neglect to mention it? They could be feeding him an update right now and then I won't hear from him for weeks. Feeling guilty, I limp to a less crowded area and sit down to call him on the cell and tell him I'm sorry, that I didn't mean to drink after promising I wouldn't. At first the other end of the line is quiet, almost as though he's surprised, then he laughs and says, "At least you called to tell me."

***

Early May pulls the temperatures solidly back into the mid to upper eighties while piling on the humidity prior to rainy season—pushing residents into air-conditioned spaces away from the tropical heat. I'm about to head out on my long-awaited senior trip with my classmates. Without Rob around and no chunks of time spent at the recording studio, it's been easier to rekindle friendships and be more involved at school. Reconnecting before the year ends has felt great, and I've been looking forward to this trip so hard.

Receiving a message that Robert is back in town puts me slightly on edge. I'm excited to see him, and I have special news to share, but I know it means my recently settled routine is about to be disrupted. Attempting normalcy, I focus on looking forward to the trip. It's a school tradition, and so many crazy stories always come out of it. Packing has been a nightmare, though. There's a dress-up event the last night to close everything out, and I haven't managed to figure out an outfit yet. It needs to be something nice, but we already returned my prom dress and we're dead broke again.

When I confess my doubts to Rob about attending because I'll look silly or underdressed, he tells me not to worry and offers to take me shopping in an hour. Sometimes his immediate empathy stuns me.

Relief washes over me as soon as I walk into a fitting room holding several options. A new outfit in hand a few hours later, I'm beaming as I carry the bags back to the cruiser. He and I climb into the middle seats with the usual entourage behind us. My new things, perfectly folded and wrapped up in tissue paper, lay near my feet in sparkling, striped gift bags. Music is pumping out of the stereo system and the day feels good. I can hear the guys making their usual dirty jokes and laughing their heads off.

As I turn to Rob to thank him, he's already eying me with a smile… expectant. His dick is out. Just out. Middle of the car. Arms stretched out to rest on the seatback.

"C'mon Zette. I got you ready for your trip. Aren't you gonna thank me?" I let my gaze sweep the car. Everyone's eyes are dodging us altogether, pretending it's not happening, trying to continue mustering up jokes. Even the driver is avoiding my eyes, refusing to tilt his head up to see me in the rearview mirror. One hand lifting off the seat, Rob gently places it on the back of my hair and pulls my head down. I'm hoping he'll let me go quick, after a little gratification, but now he's directing me, meaning he wants a complete performance. It doesn't matter to him one bit that all his friends are right there, that they can all see. My cheeks sting with heat and breathing becomes difficult as panic at my humiliation sets in. I begin to cry as I keep going.

Demetrius, Mack, the bodyguard, the other usual friends, they're all spread out in the Landcruiser. They say nothing.

No one normally says anything to me in front of Rob, so it's not exactly unexpected. Not sure what kind of discussion was had between them all early on, but generally they all avoid even looking at me, much less talking to me when Rob is around. If he goes to the bathroom (alone, mind you), it's a different story. Everyone is warmer, including me in jokes and conversation. They even take those opportunities to prank me—which means they plan ahead.

When Rob finishes, I sit up and look out the window, trying not to make any noise. I'm shaking, and they know I'm crying, but I don't want them to actually see me cry. When we arrive at the studio, everyone else fans out to couches and the live room while Rob drags me into the bathroom.

"Lizzette. Why the fuck are you crying?"

I glare at him. "Are you serious?"

"What do you mean, am I serious?" His head jerks back at the scowl I give in response. He turns to pace for a second, hands on his head, before looking me in the eyes again. "I mean, that's what you have to do. I'm your man, Zette. What are you..."

My sobbing interrupts him. Rob grasps my hips with thick hands and picks me up, setting me next to the sink, and leans his forehead against mine. Staying close, he unzips his pants, slides my dress back, pulls me tight against him, and starts fucking me loudly. I'm bouncing on the countertop, my head occasionally hitting the mirror behind. I know everyone can hear. They're in the room right outside the door. I know he's showing me how lucky I am that we're in here in private and he's not taking me out there while people are passing by.

Finishing, he zips up, stalks out of the bathroom and walks casually into the booth. I stay momentarily to fix my makeup, wiping the smears under my eyes and adding fresh mascara. As I leave the bathroom, no one looks up at me, so I pick my way over to a couch and sink into it. Everyone around me is animated, having a good time, and I'm squeezing in on myself, trying to hold it together. In my head, I'm miserable and ashamed and trying desperately to hold myself up and seem strong.

Rob is legit recording today. Currently in the live booth, he's wearing his usual "songwriting sweater" in the ninety-degree heat. His lucky sweater looks like a curse in this humidity.

His recording method requires repeating phrases and melodies quite a bit since he doesn't write anything down. One line he keeps replaying over and over again is giving me a headache because it doesn't fit the beat. It's interrupting the whole line and he can't seem to figure out where to tweak it. For the first time the entire session, I speak up.

"Rob, that one line isn't working with the rhythm. You can tell it's off, but you'd have to change it to…" He's not listening to the rest of my explanation because he's stomping out of the booth and dragging me by the arm back into the bathroom. Somehow, the sting of the slap across my face still manages to surprise me.

"I told you before, don't you ever correct me in front of people. You got that? We're recording today. It's not just you and me playing around."

"Ye-yes." I'm slightly hyperventilating and trying to catch up my breathing. "I... I said..." my chest is heaving, "I wanted it to be... good. 'Cause, you know..." I gasp for breath, "... it's better to hear now than... than somewhere else. I thought you, you would want to hear it."

"We already discussed this. I don't need nobody correcting me. I don't want nobody telling me how this line is gonna go. And don't ask me for no money for *working* on my songs. They're mine."

My eyes widen. "What? No! I've never asked you for a dollar. I was just trying to help!" This time around, I linger in the bathroom until I can face everyone, until the tears stop, and one cheek isn't way brighter than the other. Not like they'll acknowledge me anyway, so it probably doesn't matter.

After wrapping up, Rob walks me out to the car alone. Clearly, I'm not welcome to stay tonight and it's fine by me. Every few minutes the tears creep up again as we drive. He takes me to Michella's and drops me off. I don't call him.

The following day, as I'm walking up to Michella's house alone after school, her mom, Lonna, is draped out on the porch, customary glass of white wine in hand, bottle on the ground beside her. Lonna's a tiny, white Cajun woman who absolutely fits the bill of "firecracker." I can only aspire to have that much spirit when I'm older. As I walk up, she flaps a veiny hand at me and asks, "Hey honey, you know somebody named Rob?"

"Yeah. Why?"

"He's been calling all day looking for you. Driving me up the wall. I told him you were at school, but he didn't seem to catch on. Kept calling anyway."

He has other ways of getting ahold of me, meaning this was to make a point. I can't really afford to have that right now, because things at the house have already been so tense with Lonna's partner. Not entirely unexpectedly, shit hits the fan soon after that.

I currently attend school, but barely. I already know I'm not graduating and it's easier to focus on my future in music than dwell on not walking with my class. When I'm not with Rob, I've been spending too much time hiding at Michella's. Her stepmom, Miriam, didn't really want me there in the first place and it's becoming more and more strained. If it's just me, I disappear to her room and pretend I'm not there, but when Michella and I are hanging out, there's no reason to do that. We hang out in the main spaces like we've done since we were kids.

Miriam in general isn't really a happy person, unless she's with Lonna and probably just Lonna. So we're in the kitchen, Michella and Miriam and I, and I guess it's the last straw today that Michella and I are talking and laughing while she's at the table trying to read a magazine. It's a three-bedroom house, we're in the back room, and Miriam makes some snide comment about how I have to go.

Michella doesn't even hesitate. "WHAT?"

"I said it's time already. We can't keep supporting your little friend. She's gotta go."

"Oh, really?" Grabbing a broom that had been resting in a corner, Michella goes on a rampage. Stalking from room to room, she alternates between screaming at Miriam and breaking picture frames and other random items misfortunate enough to be in her way. "My best friend is not going nowhere, bitch. You're going first." Everything glass she can see is getting shattered, every freaking picture in the house, all with the stick of the broom. "*She* gotta go?" By now, Miriam has stood up and is backing away as though Michella is a wild animal. "Lissie gotta go? Not my best friend. No, *you're* going. You don't pay a goddamn thing in this house and my best friend is not going *anywhere*. You leave."

As her stepmom starts to move her mouth in some kind of defense, Michella interrupts, holding up the broom. "I run this house; my dad's social security pay for all of this. Not you."

Meanwhile, I'm literally sobbing at the doorway entrance because no one has ever stood up for me like this. This is the tenth degree, my boo, I got you forever kind of stuff. She broke the house down for me. It was still traumatic, but to Michella's credit, Miriam never messes with me again. The house vibe is awkward, naturally, after that, but Miriam leaves me alone. I think she's afraid she'll get hit with the broom next. Understandable fear.

Intentionally creating space from Miriam means seeing Rob a lot more with less restrictions on time, which he likes. When I tell him about my recently won role as a lead in *Dreamgirls*, I'm insanely proud of myself, and thrilled to be doing something more with music. Nothing like this has happened in so long.

"I don't want you doing that. I got other plans for you."

"But we aren't…"

"You're not doing it."

Unsure how to handle that response, I drop out of the musical. Now everyone is angry with me. It's not easy to recast the lead in a show, especially after rehearsals have already started. It takes a lot of shuffling. At this point, enough people at the school are frustrated with me that the principal calls my mom in for a conference. I only hear about it because I get an agitated phone call from her after, saying the principal told her, "someone is changing your daughter," and she demands to know who.

This conversation hits me hard. Harder than I expected it would. I feel like a failure because it appears I have nothing to show for any of the work I've done. I'm not graduating high school, don't have a single track out yet or even significant work on one, and now I won't be onstage either. What else is there to do than hope my career with Robert's future label starts panning out?

In the face of this feeling of defeat, I decide to work more on my own stuff, even if it's happening without support. I'm still around the studios a ton, so I'm picking up on the way things work as well as how to improve my vocal style. Also hanging around Robert a ton.

A traditional dinner at Bennigan's turns into cruising around the city, cranking up the music, and savoring a lazy day among friends. The entourage is in full hype mode, singing along, tossing out one-liners, and getting disgustingly into the yo' mama jokes. We're all into it though, and Rob's doubled up, practically shrieking with laughter. I hope he can still see the road.

When the new Mary J. Blige album comes on, it's love at first beat drop, and I insist we listen to her all the way back to the studio. Today isn't a workday—no recording goals or tracks to edit. Everyone's just messin' around, playing with lyrics, beats, and riffs. Rob's in a crazy good mood and pulls me into the bathroom for some fooling around, which ends in intimate bathroom sex. The whole vibe of today is different. I want to cut it out, fold it up, and keep it with me to take out and look at when times get harder again.

Sitting at the piano in the studio—it's just Rob and me at this point—we've got a blend of harmonizing and snorting with laughter going. Suddenly Rob's fingers quit playing notes and slide off the piano, taking my hands in his.

"Zette, you always so sweet. I would love to buy a house and settle down with you. Get married and all that." The words send lightning through me. *Excuse me?* He keeps going, "But, I'm not sure you're ready for that. You're always here at the studio and used to being in the middle of the recording process with all of us. I don't know if you're ready for change." He turns his head away, like he's thinking about something. "I don't like women in the industry, you know, women who sing for a living. Nah, don't want no part of it. I want a girl who'll stay home to take care of things, and that's their focus. Not work, especially not in this environment. I don't think you want that right now. You ain't ready to give up the life you have."

I can't keep the shock off my face. Can't keep my mouth from dropping open. All I've ever wanted is to be in the music industry. That's why we started spending time together, and he's been promising to help me for ages. Am I being told that our future, possibly even marriage, hangs in the balance of whether or not I'm ready to be a homemaker and quit the dream of singing professionally?

Doesn't take long and I'm pissed. The words hardly sputter out. "There's other things I want to do in my life right now."

Expecting a discussion, for him to push back, I'm surprised at the clipped retort. "Well, that's you." And he turns back to the music as if nothing happened.

After more hours of working out potential chords for a newly written verse, we head out so Rob can drop me home. On the way, we hit an R. Kelly tradition: fast food. We stop at the 163rd Street Wendy's. Rob and I are the only two in the Landcruiser, but his boys are right behind us in another car.

No one goes inside the building, we just park in the parking lot and all Rob's buddies jump out to catch women on the way back to their cars. They have this scheme where they say, "Oh, we with R. Kelly," because it draws women like flies.

I'm sittin' in the front of the Landcruiser next to Rob, with Biggie playing in the background. Our current jam song is "Big Poppa." We're both singing along and waiting for the one line where we shout, "'Cause I see some ladies tonight that should be havin' my baby... Uh... baby... uh." The moment cracks us up laughing until I notice him just looking at me. At first, I think it's overflow from the conversation earlier, maybe some kind of sweetness about our potential life together, then I realize he's holding his dick out above his waistband, giving me that face that means he's expecting it.

"Come on. I want it now. Right now, wit' you."

Taking in the scene around us, I could practically touch the people right outside the door, they're so close. They can definitely see in.

"Nah, I'm not doin' it."

Disappointment flickers as he waves to his guys and squeals out of the parking lot. I already know what happened. I didn't perform, so I'm done for the day.

"These jokers, man," Rob says as he slows down for a turn, "They tell 'em they're with me. Those girls don't give a shit about them. They're just around because I am." I know he's right, and that he's probably headed back to Wendy's once I'm out of the car.

CHAPTER 13

The end of the school year hits with draining humidity and stifling uncertainty after not technically graduating with my class. I don't stick around to finish my credits over the summer. Things at Michella's have been tense for so long, it makes more sense to move to New York and try to hack it out in a new place, close to family. She also met someone already she's cozying up with, so branching out by myself seems ideal. I'll be staying with my Aunt Carmen in the projects on the lower east side of Manhattan, along with my cousin Tamika and Uncle Otis. Also, and importantly, I'll finally be in close proximity to my older sister again.

Arriving in the city, I waste no time in seeking my sibling out for advice about my love and work relationships with Rob. One perk of moving to New York City is supposed to be that it'll be easier to see him and be "with" him. Plus, I'm close to so much music, which is all I want to pursue, with or without Robert's help.

I tell my sister about Rob—the highs and lows, roller coasters, in-betweens, marriage thoughts, everything. Right now, she's the only person in my family I trust to know about all this. Taking on the role of protective older sibling, when Demetrius reaches out, she talks to him and listens as he explains that Rob wants me to visit him in Chicago just to see what it's like. I'm old enough to fly alone and he'll pay for the flights. All I have to do is call Rob's assistant at Jive

Records to request dates and times and I'm golden. Set. My sister is reluctant, but I'm excited. One chapter of my life is closing and the next is opening up to something new.

The push in Chicago's direction is also coming from my home life in New York. Aunt Carmen and I have a great connection when it's just us, but I intruded on her relationship with her daughter, my cousin Tamika. When I first arrive, it's a source of major contention. Jealous of the bond my aunt and I have always shared, my cousin starts acting out to the point of aggression and hostility. Not towards my aunt, just me. One severe mood brings her into our shared room with a butcher knife, totally upset about something to the point of appearing unhinged. She's holding it up at me and I'm afraid she's going to stab me. I stand up, hands in the air, trying to talk her down. She rolls her eyes, lowers the knife, and punches me instead. This prompts a short stay with my sister until I leave for Chicago.

Flying to O'Hare from LaGuardia Airport (or LGA) brings more relief than nerves. Everything in New York has been a struggle lately, so a direct flight, followed by a limo waiting for me outside the Chicago airport, brings a smile to my face. Leather seats never felt so good. Nodding my head at the driver as he shuts my door with a crisp click, life finally feels okay. I'm in Chicago on my way to meet Rob, far away from my crazy hometown and the crazy new town. Pretty sure nothing could kill my vibe right now.

Dropped off at a towering hotel, windows looming so high they cut off the sunshine, I walk up to the desk and nervously state my name. Rob never mentioned checking in without him present, but the front desk agent smiles and hands me a key. As I close my hand around it, she repeats my name and then a random-sounding host name the room is listed under. No one asks for identification or any further information about me, so, clutching the key, I head to the elevator across the lobby and up to the room. I'm still celebrating on top of the bed when Rob calls and I flop down on the soft pillows to listen. He says he'll be by in a few hours and to order whatever I want in the meantime. Hello, fancy life.

After being pushed out of my own mother's house— both belongings and me tossed out like garbage—openly rejected within the walls of my best friend's home, then held at knifepoint by my cousin, it's hard not to feel like I've struck gold. Not with money, but affirmation, acceptance. Rob wants me here. Someone truly appreciates my presence. And when has that happened before? I have a place to be, where I fit, and it's all that matters. I eat dinner in the room and fall asleep in a contented food coma, waiting for Rob.

About eight hours later, sometime around 3 a.m., his voice wakes me up from a heavy sleep.

"Babe! Zette. You awake?" Smiling, I sit up. Some of the lights are still on. I was so tired I didn't notice, just conked out. He slides his pants off in the semidarkness and settles next to me on the bed. "I couldn't wait to see you."

Instead of a welcome kiss, he's hard and making himself harder. His free hand motions at me. "Come here." With a grin, he's stroking my arm and softly pulling me over. I know what he wants. "Be good, baby." Hands guide my face down and instead of the reunion I imagined, I'm giving him the head he always craves. He stays twenty minutes or so after finishing to ask me about my flight and fill me in on current projects, then says he has to go.

"Wait, what? But I came here to see you."

"I know, and I'll be back tomorrow. I'm writing a song for someone big, huge thing, and I'm trying to bang it out as fast as possible. Been hella busy with it. Lots of pressure, ya know? Just wait here in the room for me and I'll meet you when I'm done." The goodbye hug is brief—a peck on the lips and he's out the door. I head to the bathroom to brush my teeth before collapsing into bed again and letting sleep soothe the cut of disappointment.

The next morning arrives, fresh and bright, but Rob doesn't. I order a meal up to the room, watch the streets from the window for a while, turn on the TV, anything to get my mind off where he might be. When I haven't heard from him by midafternoon, I start calling and continue doing so throughout the evening. How many calls will he ignore? Ten... twenty... more?

Later that night when he finally picks up, clearly unhappy, he says his brother Carey was arrested, then cuts me short before I can ask about it. Sensing Rob's frustration is verging on an angry meltdown, I stay quiet while he gripes briefly about not having time for this and cuts the line off. I don't see him until Sunday, a full second day later, the day I'm supposed to leave.

My return flight to New York takes off in a few hours, so my bags are mostly packed and ready at the end of the bed. Thinking Rob might drop by in the short time remaining, my cutest outfit lays folded on top, waiting for after I shower. It's looking like the preparation was in vain until I hear the key click and Rob bursts through the door.

Unlike the apology I was expecting for being left alone here all weekend, he stalks into the room, yelling and cursing, telling me I'm in his business too much and need to stay out, learn my place, figure my shit out on my own. Starting to cry, I grab my bag from the end of the bed and set it on a lounge chair by the entry hall before shutting myself in the bathroom to shower. At least the warm water washes away the tears, giving me a chance to recover before facing the verbal onslaught again.

When I open the bathroom door, my stuff is gone, so I wander back towards the bedroom area looking for it. Rob has set the bags next to the bed, and as I go to pick them up again, he rips the towel off my hips and starts running his hands up and down my sides. Words come tumbling out of him, telling me he's sorry, that I need to be more understanding, that it's okay. The heavy, familiar hands slide down to my thighs as Rob kneels and tries to please me, pulling my body in when I step back. Then I'm lifted up and strong arms place me on the bed, basketball shorts slide off, and he's having sex with me. I can feel the anger and emotion in the tension of his body. His position over me prevents me from moving. I'm held in place, and everything is intense, rough.

My mind drifts to separate me from the pain, and next thing I know, I'm staring at the ceiling while Rob rests his head on my chest, apologizing over and over. With his weight still on me, the temporary numbness of my lower body hasn't registered yet.

"It's okay," I hear myself whisper. My top half feels disconnected from the bottom, like it's someone else down there who hurts. I watch the ceiling, listening to his apologies and uneven breath. When he pushes himself up, I have no will to move. Everything feels stuck. Awareness still lingers only in my upper body, so I lay there in silence while he pulls clothing back on and answers his mobile. A girl's voice sounds through the other side. They're chatting and laughing. He asks when she's coming to sing backup.

"Y'all need to come, n****. I need every one of you out here." He's perched on the corner of the bed, totally engrossed. I'm forgotten.

I get up, take my things to the living room, get dressed, and leave. My ride to O'Hare is paid for through the room account, but I don't have cab fare for the ride home in New York. From the airport, I catch a cab, pretending to have money, and ditch it when we pull into my neighborhood.

Then I curl up on my bed and cry for days.

Once Rob apologizes—by calling excessively until I answer the phone—we start talking regularly again and fall into a routine of me visiting him in Chicago every other weekend or so. This is how the rest of the summer is spent: in a dreamy state of weekends spent with Rob making music, and slogging through my half existence in New York, where I shuffle through part-time jobs and look forward to my next trip out.

***

Late July in Chicago is hot but nearly feels refreshing after the sweltering humidity of New York. I hardly notice anyway. After several visits to the Windy City and only seeing the inside of a hotel room or the McDonald's down the street, I've finally been invited to Rob's house. By house, I mean this giant church someone turned into a house. It's supposed to be pretty striking, like an enormous structure to take in.

He's acting even more paranoid than usual on the ride there, insisting my head stays all the way down, completely out of view the entire time, regardless of traffic or location. Like a truck of paparazzi could sidle up beside us at a light and still not be able to get a good look at anything more than the back of my head, which is currently shoved between my legs, hovering right above my sandaled feet. Rob re-explains avoiding potential photographers for maybe the thousandth time. So much for seeing Chicago.

True to the gossip, the house is impressive, overwhelmingly big. Walking through, there's every gadget and style of room you could think of. Robert is clearly pleased at my astonishment. I can tell he's excited too, showing me around. There are three levels, and he pulls me up the stairs to the second floor into a room with bunkbeds. A massive window on one side looks out on a single, large palm tree. Interesting.

Gently taking my hand, Rob walks me over to the window.

"I put this here because it reminds me of you."

"What?"

"It reminds me of you and me, us, back in Miami."

The sweet gesture floods me with warmth, and I let go of the car-ride frustration. He's just watching out for me. He's been thinking about me this whole time, even when I didn't always hear from him.

Abruptly, he's on to the next thing, guiding me to the main living room, running around, turning on music equipment and looking for something. Motioning at me to take a seat on the couch, I sink onto a corner cushion and prop my elbow on the armrest, watching him. He grins over at me.

"Michael Jackson doin' this song right here."

This grabs my attention, but it's not Michael Jackson's voice that comes through the speakers when he presses play, it's Rob's. Bobbing along to his own voice with his chest all puffed up, I've never seen him so proud of his work. I've also never been allowed to listen in on one of his reference tracks. He writes music for people all the time, but he's never played any of it for me before. I wonder why this particular song. Did he bring me to his house just so I could hear it?

"I started writing these lyrics when you were in Miami and I had to be in Chicago. It was hard to get ahold of you for a while. I missed you."

Briefly stunned, I look up and our eyes lock.

"This song, it's about us. The things we went through."

The rush in my head is like the beginning of a roller coaster: dizzying anticipation. I've never been this central to someone's life before. The heady feeling sinks down to my toes until my whole body seems to hum. So this is love.

I almost stand up and leap into his arms, but it would kill the mood, plus I'm still lightheaded so I'd probably just fall over first. Smiling at me, he starts moving around, bopping his head to the music and singing along silently. His excitement is infectious and I'm beaming back at him from my spot on the couch. Ambling towards me, I wait for him to plop down next to me, cozy up together to our song. Instead, he swings his hips to face me and pushes at his waistband.

"Okay, get down on your knees, babe. I need you right now." The direct order takes a second to process. It's not until I look up again and see him standing there, legs apart and holding himself ready that it hits me. I freeze.

My submission is his favorite part of our relationship. He thought, genuinely thought, this would make me happy, to do this to him during a song written while thinking of me. I'm happy for him, and that he's excited, and because he loves Michael Jackson. This is an incredible opportunity for him. It even sounds like Michael Jackson adores him too, but… why would I want this?

Impatient, his hand slides behind my head to coax me to the ground and I'm down on my knees again. No… please no. Not this. Not like this. There's nothing romantic, no sign of affection, nothing really about me after all, just our twisted relationship glorified in lyrical form. Played out in a continual act of submission.

When he's done, I pretend to keep listening as I stare down at the floor. Tears trickle as I shift my legs to cross them, arms bent across my waist, squeezing my middle. Rob seems to think I'm overwhelmed with tears of joy, but my body is tight as can be, trying to pull in and in and in. What a confused person. I'm not sure he's in love with me as much as what he can do with me, how I'm there for *him*.

On the route back to the hotel, Rob's concern about being followed hits an all-time high. I'm crouched so far down and forward, I'm practically off the seat. If we get in an accident, the glove compartment is going to break my neck, if not my entire back.

It's starting to sink in, the idea that this will never be the relationship I want it to be. Despite putting on a happy-go-lucky air when we get back, my insides feel like they're being slowly crushed. I love him. Dearly. God, I love him so much.

This love is going to kill me if I'm not careful.

CHAPTER 14

The beauty of New York in the fall is doing nothing to improve the gloom that sets in after my most recent trip to Chicago. All the giddiness of visiting Rob has grown stale lately. It doesn't feel like I fit in his life, and I'm not sure he wants me to. Calls are less consistent, and he hasn't invited me out to join him for over a month.

The constant shifting back and forth between here and there meant I couldn't take on full-time work and left my part-time jobs in precarious positions—most of which I lost. Finding new work that pays decently has been a struggle, and I'm not the only one hurting this season. My aunt and cousin are feeling it too.

Life at the apartment has become unbearable. It's freezing. We hardly eat. There's no money, so there's no groceries. Aunt Carmen has her supply of beer in the fridge, but that's about it. She and Uncle Otis are both alcoholics, and generally Carmen's a happy one, but lately they've spent the evenings fighting about one thing or another. I spend my days applying for new jobs and not hearing back. Meanwhile my weight drops below a hundred pounds. I'm usually tiny, but not this tiny. Dating a successful music artist but can't afford to eat… Go figure.

Rob calls out of nowhere, wanting to meet me in New York. This is new. For some reason, the shift in settings is getting my nerves all riled up. He's coming for a show, not for me, but we're going to meet at a hotel in midtown. My stomach buzzes as I search for an outfit. There haven't been many occasions in New York to dress up and I don't fit most of my clothes anymore. Not without looking scrawny. My cousin Tamika is with me and offers to wait downstairs or in a nearby restaurant so I can meet Rob in private. That way she and I can head home together later. When Rob doesn't show up within the hour, I go down and tell her not to stick around. It's going to be a while.

Not a new sensation, being left in a hotel room to wait, but still not a great one. Old flickers of disappointment start rising up. I know he likes to keep me waiting to see if I stick around for it. The aching familiarity makes me feel sad and spent. I curl up on the bed, careful not to muss the makeup or hair, and don't even notice my eyes casually drifting shut.

Fists drumming on the door disrupt my nap. By the time I cross the room to open it, Rob's smacking the wood with both hands like he's high out of his mind. Lumbering in, the door shuts behind him as I switch a single lamp on. Squinting his eyes as though the brightness in the room is too much, he gives me a good look up and down.

"You don't look too good, Zette." My hands immediately fly to my ribs, holding them protectively as I look down, examining my body. "Are you okay?"

"Not really eating lately. Some days there's nothing *to* eat. I don't have any money put away and I can't find work."

Head tilting to the side, he raises an arm to point at me dramatically, swaying a bit as he does it. "That's yo' problem. Your *pride*. You need to put that pride in yo' pocket."

The only thing keeping the fury contained is knowing how bad it could turn out if I yell at him. I don't have a job because I couldn't steadily keep one when I was visiting him in Chicago all the time. Now I'm left with a part-time gig pressing and ironing men's shirts at a little designer boutique. Rob was my priority for a long time, but I'm starting to forget why it seemed so important.

"Babe, just ask me for whatever you need."

"Whatever I need? I went to Chicago so many times to be with you and you would disappear for days. I didn't always have money to eat then either, even when I was there *for you*. Sometimes there wasn't even a credit card on the damn room."

"Sorry, uh... thas not my fault." His head dips forward and straightens again. "It's Mack's fault, not makin' sure the card is on your room." Silence lulls between us, then he staggers towards me. Approaching me with open arms, his words turn to silly, drunk chatter, but it's sweet. He asks for forgiveness, apologizes with severe intensity, and reassures me I'll be taken care of in the future. The crumbling on my part is pretty much foreseen. As soon as I'm smiling too and he's clearly forgiven, a confident hand takes mine and tows me over to the bed, where he lays down and pulls off his shorts.

"You know what to do, Zette."

Of course I do. His favorite. When it's over, Rob jumps up, slides athleticwear back on, and heads to the door. Pausing in the doorway, he turns to look back at me.

"You can stay here the night. The hotel is paid for."

And he's gone.

I invite Tamika back. We watch movies on pay-per-view and order a bunch of food so we can have plenty of leftovers to take home. It's the most I've eaten in ages, and we'll all be able to eat for a week.

There are more visits, more phone calls, but by late December, they've all dwindled down to just about nothing. Rob seems to have disappeared from my life again. I don't have the physical energy anymore to fight it. The current weather matches my shitty mood: a blizzard overtakes New York. Stinging winds and icy streets keep everyone cooped up inside—more time to wander past the phone and ruminate on why it's not ringing.

Right as the storm prepares to hold New Yorkers captive indoors for a solid chunk of days, my Uncle Al and his wife Ingrid help Tamika and I move into Co-op City with them in the Bronx. This is moving up for us. Concern had been growing about our living situation and lack of food over in the Lower East Side.

Al is a retired paramedic and Ingrid is a no-nonsense powerhouse who always has her shit together. But she's not meant to be taking care of us, just offering a leg up. I like to sit and talk with her at the table as she smokes imported cigarettes, long and skinny. Her other hand rests on the table with long, painted nails which clack against the table as she talks. She's the classiest lady I know. I want to be her and own a fly white Cadillac like hers. I imagine myself that put together someday.

Ingrid quickly becomes a mother-like figure to me, and we get close. She talks to me about life and love, jobs, and the gritty details of making it through the rough times. She always tells me, "You're a winner, Lizzette. Stick with the winners."

Since flights to Chicago aren't happening, I share a room with Tamika at the new place and look for a job when the snow eases up in January. Despite the ups and downs of the last few months, when Rob gets antsy for me to come visit in the spring, I start up my usual weekend excursions to Chicago again. What's it take for a girl to learn, huh? I'm about to find out.

CHAPTER 15

"I took a test, Rob. I'm pregnant."

No response.

"Robert?" I wait. Aunt Carmen already told him I'd missed my period. Then apparently called him up, asking what he was going to do about it. That's why I'm here at her place, figuring out what to do next. I don't want anyone else to know.

"I don't like that. I don't like girls that are pregnant."

"Uhhh." What am I supposed to say now? "Okay."

An exasperated sigh blows into my earpiece, followed by Rob's "practiced" deep voice he uses for ensuring audience attention. He doesn't need to use it; he's already got my attention. "I mean, you need to come here, Zette. I need you to come to me, now." Why is he so terrified? It's a baby, not a nuclear bomb. "I want you to come tomorrow."

I tell him I'm not sure and hang up.

The remainder of the spring and summer had been wonderful, so carefree it almost hurts to think about. This was not my smoothest transition into the fall.

Rob calls back the next day and Titi Carmen answers the phone. She reminds him loudly that this all started when I was underage, so he doesn't have a lot of leeway here. While she threatens R. Kelly and chides him about the inappropriateness of his behavior, I listen in the hall, tucked behind the doorframe.

"None of my business? That's my blood. It is my damned business. And yes, we're sure. She took the test after missing her period. I told you." Poking her head around the corner, she passes over the phone with the heavy sigh of someone who just finished a marathon. "He said he wants you to go over there. But if I were you," a comforting hand slides onto my shoulder, "I wouldn't go. Because he's gonna make you have an abortion. Just so you know. He doesn't want the child."

And I thought my panicking had already hit its limit. *Nah, girl, it's just starting.* Shakily holding the phone up to my ear, Robert's voice creaks through the static. From the sound of it, Ingrid struck some measure of fear in him. He's clearly shaken.

I look up at my aunt who is leaning with one shoulder against the wall, watching the whole event play out between narrowed eyes, a cold Budweiser slunk into one relaxed hand. Standing there, uncertain, hearing his voice in my ear saying he wants me there with him tomorrow, wants me as soon as possible, all I can do is say yes. I'm crying, and it's probably not the best idea, but I agree to call his travel agent and take the next reasonable flight out.

Endless worries race through my head. What would Michella think about my being pregnant? Or my sister. They're going to be so disappointed in me. I can't even scrape a family together. My aunt knows, but that's okay. I trust her. Mom can't know. She also can't find out through the grapevine, or the media. That would be the worst. At least I'm of age now, so it's less of a scandal, but she'd know I'd been lying to her for months about everything else.

Rob didn't offer an, "I'm sorry, we'll figure it out together." No, "Don't stress, it'll be okay." So it feels like the entire situation has collapsed on my shoulders alone, and I can't carry all of it. Sleeping tonight seems impossible. But laying in the dark, rubbing my lower abdomen and the baby

I know rests underneath, I manage to calm down enough to lose myself to blissful unconsciousness.

The next day, I board an American Airlines flight to O'Hare. I spend the majority of my time in the air being a total nervous wreck. The anxiety only increases as we close in on Chicago. Of course, I wasn't ready for or planning on a child. That Rob might even think that is insane. Dreams of my singing career are floating out the window. I'm young. Without the right support, this could change everything and put me entirely out of the running for a legit vocal career. Each time the dark, straining knot in my stomach starts to ease and I almost doze off, it tightens again with a cruel ache. I stare out the plane window, trying to push everything out of my head until I at least see Robert's reaction to the news in person. This flight feels like it's lasting a lifetime.

By the time I'm crossing my way back over a boarding ramp alongside other passengers, the internal battle has left me dazed. My body seems hollow, almost unreal, like this isn't really happening. Looking for the limo driver holding a "Martinez" sign is trickier when my eyes keep blurring with tears.

Be strong. You gotta get it together. Hold it in, swallow it down, and stand straight. There's no other way to get through it. Spotting my driver, I wave and allow myself to be escorted into the expansive vehicle. The man offers to take my bag, but it's small, so I keep it with me.

Despite thinking Rob might want to keep this situation super hush-hush, we, once again, do not pull up to one of his private houses. Surprise, surprise, I'm dropped off at a hotel alone, and Rob isn't there. On the upside, his manager remembered to include a credit card on file this time with an open invitation to order anything I'd like up to the room.

Pregnant and craving, this sounds like heaven. Its's a relief to finally be taken care of somewhat.

It's late afternoon when I check into the room, but Rob doesn't swing by until midnight. The half-hearted hug and hello automatically put me on edge. He's hardly looking me in the eyes. No conversation takes place in the room aside from a quick, "All right, let's go to the studio," almost as soon as he arrives. The lack of affection tugs at me after coming all this way. My hair is done up the way he likes and I'm wearing a long, stunning summer dress with brown sandals. He doesn't seem to notice. Despite the awkward circumstances, I feel pretty and elegant, but the blatant indifference is taking me down a couple notches.

At the recording studio, I'm made to wait while Rob works on a track. In addition, I'm also expected to sit here and listen to him coach the young girl joining him on said track.

I watch her. Edges of short blonde bangs are continuously swept behind an ear with her free, bangled hand as she sings something about how all she wants is to hump and bounce. Clever. She's failing to hit a note over and over in the chorus at the same spot, and I can't help thinking this is so messed up. What the hell is going on? Rob and I have been working on music together for a while now and I'm still not singing on any of his recordings. Now this kid is here, and I'm supposed to just watch from this stupid black couch? The girl isn't even responsive to his critiques and keeps making the same dumb mistake. It's infuriating. I find the correct note in my head. I'm burning to sing it correctly with him over her.

Steve, the tech engineer, plops his chin in his hand in frustration as she hits it flat again. So now I have to wait until the newbie gets it right before Rob can talk to me about our child. A few choice words fall out of my mouth before I can stop them, and Steve turns around, locking eyes with me in slight surprise. My anger melts away when his face fills with sadness and concern. That look unnerves me more than anything.

Rob stops the session. I'm still strewn across the couch, but his head jerks roughly to the right as he walks past—my cue to follow him outside.

To the fire escape. Great place to talk about having a child.

He starts. "I don't think this is a good idea."

"No shit."

Unusually blunt for me. His face slackens in surprise. "It's not like you to get like this. And what was that back in the studio?"

"Hm. Well, watch which way you want me to get." I can't do this. I need to get the words out before they make me sick. "I don't believe in abortion, you know, I grew up Catholic. There's too many… Rob, I can't. I can't do it." Salty tears spill out of my eyes, smudging makeup down my cheeks.

He's kneading his hands together, his thumb tracing his palm hard, like he's rubbing something sticky off. A sign he's really trying to hold back right now. I can see the tension in his knuckles, in the way the veins are slowly rising to the top.

"You're going to ruin your career, Lizzette."

"What career?" I demand.

"I'm getting it together! When I have my own record label, I'll make you an artist. It's gonna happen." Flustered, his words stumble, unsteady. "Shit. You… you're going to ruin your body. What will you do then?"

"I don't know *what* I'm going to do." This shuts him up. I can tell he doesn't want to talk anymore.

Not looking at me, he says, "I'll sign you when I get my label," glances back once at my stomach, then shakes his head and drifts back into the studio in silence. I break down. I want to die. Knowing it would be ideal for him if I left, I decide to stay. Working angry might inspire him. Has before. Tired and emotionally drained, sleep comes to me quickly on the studio couch.

Waking up to the commotion of a bunch of people after a talk like that... not exactly ideal, but here they are, at Rob's invitation. Minus that Rob isn't here. He left without me again. Next thing I know, Steve is telling me I should go, that Demetrius will take me back to the hotel. Steve has taken me home on many occasions when I've been forgotten about and left solo at the studio. Helping me up, he searches for my purse with me until we find it under a chair. As he rests it in my hands, he whispers, "Don't be with him. There are so many different girls." Then he guides me out and passes me off to Demetrius. I cry the entire ride back to the hotel. Who cares anymore what people think? This is my fucking life.

Pacing back and forth in my hotel room, I try to think of ways to make this better. Apologize? Probably not enough. Not sure Rob would even come here for just that. Fall on my knees and beg for mercy? Nah, it would turn into a weird sex thing and I'm already feeling destroyed by all of this. Let my aunt threaten him a little more... tempting, but I want to be with him, to make him happy, not drive him away.

I can't stay still, so I head downstairs, charge cigarettes to the room, and smoke outside, sucking in nicotine like it might save my nerves from complete decay. I never smoke. And I realize now is the worst time to do it, but everything feels frayed and falling apart. The same mantra flies through my head every minute: *You can't lose him. You need him.*

My fingers continue to dial Rob's number over and over. The wall of silence is shattering what little sanity I still have left at this point. I call Michella, who picks up. Between my choking tears and borderline hysterical thought process, she manages to get the basic idea.

"Lizzette! Get. The. Hell. Out of there!" The wind is picking up and I sink down against the wall. "I can help you. Please, let me help you."

"I... I don't have money to get home. I don't have a way to get money." Saying it out loud starts to bring my thoughts back in order. *I don't even know if I can get out of here.*

That night, there's no word from Rob. He stays elsewhere, doesn't call. The following afternoon, he arrives without notice, trailed by his manager, Derrel McDavid. A single knock at the door is the only indication of their presence before barging in. They seem ready for something big.

The spiel Rob throws at me is basically the same as the other night, so I interrupt. "You told me you would help me with a music career, and you didn't! You can't use that 'supposed' career that *never happened* as a reason now to get what works best for *you*." Unsurprisingly, this remark sends the conversation spiraling into a full-on fight. Derrel gently tugs on his arm, pulling him out to the hallway to calm down. Despite tip-toeing a tad closer, I can't make out their low voices. Derrel has always been nice to me, but I don't trust him, especially after they saunter back in for Rob's final comment before they leave.

Disturbingly calm, Rob looks at me and says in a quiet voice, "I'm going to come back tomorrow, to be here for you." The instant change in demeanor is throwing me off. "And we'll take you to the doctor." The tension cracks as they glance at each other and both break down into uncontrollable laughter. They leave without saying goodbye, but I can hear their chuckles echoing in the hallway.

Demetrius scurries in with a concerned frown. "Are you okay?" I'm trying not to let my tears turn into full-on wailing that guests will be able to hear on other floors. He settles down next to me and we talk about the other night, how awful it was, and how stressed I am at this point. Sharp pains in my abdomen and lower back are starting to drown out my thoughts.

"I don't know what's wrong. I'm starting to have pretty intense cramps."

"Then I'm taking you to the doctor. Now."

The hospital is a blur of questions, nurses, cold tiles, and endless waiting. Somewhere between the commotion and the foggy lull from the meds they gave me, someone hollers that we need to test for HIV. Sorry, what?

It's negative, thankfully, and I notice Rob has finally shown up. The hospital staff is trying to figure out how many weeks along I am. It sounds like an auction—the nurses just throwing out numbers. *Five weeks! Six! Okay, maybe early on six! Early, early on six!* (Good thing we're so well informed now). They tell us there's nothing they can do at the moment and send me home. Home as in, the hotel where Rob drops me off and leaves me to cope by myself. For the next *four days.*

Two days in, I find myself staring out at the world in fear from the thick hotel windows, waiting for Rob to call while the pain gets worse and rest feels nearly impossible. Demetrius continues to make me feel strung along on our phone calls, saying he's not sure where Rob went, and my anxiety grows with every passing minute. This is not normal pregnancy pain. I need help.

After crawling to the shower with Michella on the phone and blacking out, I wake up hours later to blood everywhere. It's incredible I haven't bled out. Everything around me is stained black and rust. On weakened legs, I attempt to stagger out of the shower, but end up lying on the cold tile, stomach pressed to the cool flooring. Fancy tile with an ornate design. Here I am in this fancy place, gilded with money and hopes for a better life, and I know, I just know without anyone telling me, I've lost my baby.

On the fourth day since the hospital visit, the hallway door creaks open, and Rob pokes his head in. For two days I've been too exhausted to so much as move. My deadened limbs drape across the linens, and I know the soft fabric is permanently soiled from my sweat and blood. The room probably reeks with the iron stench of old blood mixed with salty tears and fluids. Somehow, I don't care. Emptiness has taken over. There's nothing left, just a limp body sprawled on a pile of expensive cushions.

The sharp pain has dulled. Feelings are long since gone, and nothing penetrates the dizzying fog in my head.

I hardly notice I'm being taken to the hospital. Am I carried away? Do I walk out of there with assistance? Do they whisk me away in a wheelchair? There's no memory of it, just the blur of being in the room followed by the more substantial and chaotic blur of being back in the hospital with a nurse saying there's nothing they can do but stabilize me. Only me. No baby.

Did Rob know this might happen? Is that why he was gone for so long when he knew I was pregnant and sick? Well, I'm not pregnant anymore. Deep down, I already knew, but hearing it said aloud is like having the nurse shout it into a massive canyon where the words shout back at you over and over. Each echo a reminder pounding in my head that my baby is lost, lost, lost.

CHAPTER 16

Dark, dreamless sleep turns to nightmares about miscarrying over and over again. When I fully wake, still in the hospital, Rob visits me. He doesn't apologize. Instead, he brings a giant teddy bear. This happens a lot. Not sure why it's a thing, but he's really into buying me stuffed animals as a substitute for his words. There are flowers in his hand as well when he sits down beside the bed, his face unreadable.

"I'm sorry, Zette."

I don't respond, can't respond. Even if I tried, there are no words for this.

"You know, I just, I had people here in Chicago to work on stuff, and we were in a recording session for a long time."

Tears start falling; I can't help it. I was alone for my miscarriage because Rob was in a surprise recording session for four days and couldn't check on his pregnant girlfriend right after a hospital visit? A meeting so important, he couldn't even pick up the phone.

"Babe, I couldn't leave…"

"Robert, just leave it alone." The snap in my voice shocks him into silence. "It wasn't meant to be." I roll to face the window so I don't have to look at him. "This. *This* is how you treat me after so long?" He doesn't say anything, but I don't really expect him to. At last, I hear his steps shuffle and dim as he walks away. When Demetrius arrives to check on me, I ask for money to get back to New York to be with family, and he complies on the spot. It's not like Rob is going to be waiting around my room while I recover.

There are no adequate words for how difficult it is just to be alive in the days that follow. A lot of time is spent in my bed at Ingrid's place in New York, burrowing under thick blankets, trying to forget reality. Lights are always turned off because the dimness helps. You can get lost in darkness; it's harder in the bright of day.

Leaving bed is an effort, but leaving the room feels impossible. The only moments I really consider leaving are when I look down through the window and imagine jumping in front of a truck. This thought needles at my brain far too often. Blissful forgetting, though, just being done... it's so tempting. If I had more energy, I would probably be more proactive about it. As it is, I rarely leave the safety of bed and even sit down in the shower. Teetering over to the bathroom requires enormous effort. Sitting down halfway to the door helps, or lying down for a moment isn't so bad.

I need to get back to work, help out with the bills, get my own place. Every day, suicide looks more and more promising as all the delayed responsibilities tumble over me like a wave. My chest hurts as though my heart actually broke that day in the hospital. Entire nights of sobbing leave me feeling dry, like the moisture in my head is all gone and there's nothing left to give. This is then replaced by dry-eyed staring at the wall.

With time, I start to move around a bit, open the blinds more, and chat with Michella on the phone, nursing comfort from our talks. Thoughts about dying are still frequent, but the sharpness of the fantasies has dulled. Eventually, life starts going back to normal, or whatever kind of "normal" this is. I find a new job and new ways to distract myself from the hurt.

Rob has called my phone a few times and wants me to come back to Chicago. Every once in a while, I talk with him briefly, but generally I ignore it.

A few weeks before Thanksgiving, Rob calls the apartment and I happen to pick up.

"Zette, you're gonna hear some things," he mutters in a low tone I can hardly hear.

"What things?"

"Um... Bad things." Is he crying?

"Just tell me what's going on, Rob," I whisper, hoping no one else in the house can hear me.

"Just promise me you'll stick by me."

"I promise. Wha—"

He hangs up.

Ingrid suggests I invite Rob and the entourage for Thanksgiving, so I call and call and leave messages. No answer. I'm assuming it has something to do with the cryptic phone conversation. Maybe it really is something bad.

Thanksgiving Day comes and goes with all the fixings, plus cheesecake, which I've been getting really into making lately. Everyone is together, and any tension between family evaporates as we fill our stomachs and chat closely, comforted by one another's presence. But I can't blow away the cloud hanging over me from my conversation with Rob. I'm worried.

A couple days later, he finally calls back, asking about my Thanksgiving.

"It was really good. The family all got together, made my own cheesecake and everyone loved it."

"Why didn't you invite me?"

This elicits a huge sigh on my end. "Really, Rob? I been calling for days, running up my aunt and uncle's phone bill on that three-one-two number that *never answers*." Instead of admitting he's avoided the phone like the plague, he turns it around on me for not calling enough, or at the right times.

"You could have found a way to get ahold of me," he says.

"I was already calling and leaving messages, plus I didn't think you would come anyway."

***

Directly after the holiday, I meet with an agent couple in New York who are looking to snag a deal for a singer, preferably with Motown Records. A friend gave them my tape, and now their only hesitation is my relationship with Robert. We meet at a coffee shop where they sit me down and say they need to know exactly what is going on between the two of us. They're worried his preferences will affect my career decisions. I'm reluctant to talk to them about it, especially since I haven't seen him since the miscarriage, but also don't want to start a professional relationship without complete trust on both sides.

After listening to me ramble for a while, their faces have taken on a distinctly familiar mask of unease. The woman rests her hand on mine as she tells me she's so sorry, but I need to understand that Rob will not act in my best interests, only his own, and it would be better for me to get out now instead of later down the road. Judgment sinks into my skin as I try to sort through my emotions and explain my past decisions. I start to break down, insisting as the tears start streaming that he isn't all bad.

"Lizzette, has he ever truly done anything for your career? To help you?" The question catches me by surprise. "I see you struggling to get by, and there's nothing wrong with that, but… R. Kelly is R. Kelly, and everyone in the industry knows what he likes and knows he does things for himself first and foremost." Now my sobbing is in full effect and I'm stuttering, trying to get words out to deny it, but I can't. "We want to help you. We set up a meeting for you with Motown Records, and they're very interested."

These two are right. I need to do this myself and shake off the expectation that Rob is going to sign me. Also, to make sure he doesn't prevent me from taking my chance when I have it. Nodding, I agree to not see Robert anymore. Reassured, they nod back as they tell me they'll be in touch to make sure I have the exact date and time for the meeting.

"Your voice has a strong presence, and you have a beautiful look. We want you to know we think you can make it, but you have to let him go. That kind of relationship is going to hold you back. It's going to interfere. We've seen it before." They both offer sympathetic smiles and leave with one more promise to let me know about the meeting as soon as possible.

I'm working at the United Jewish Federation as a telemarketer when the call from my supervisor comes to see him in his office. Hovering at his door, I wait in silence as he squints down at a note and says that someone named "Robert" has been calling all day for me. My throat clenches and I wonder how many times he called. He can be persistent. I hope I'm not about to lose my job.

"I'm so sorry. It won't happen again."

My supervisor raises an eyebrow and holds out the slip of paper with a phone number written across it. "No, it's okay. Just make sure you call him back, so he stops."

I rack my brain as I walk back to my desk. I never told Rob where I worked. Not even the previous jobs, because then he didn't care. These past several weeks I've been trying to separate from it all, meaning he tracked me down somehow to get ahold of me here. Not unusual given his history, but it's not like he's reached out much lately by calling the apartment. Why would he try to contact me elsewhere?

When I get home, I tentatively dial the number. Swallowing panic, each ringing trill seems to take forever. My heart jumps when I hear the classic "click" signaling someone's picked up.

"Rob? I heard you've been call—"

"Zette! I really need to see you." He's crying, and mumbling something, but I can't make it out.

"What's wrong?"

"I… I can't talk about it over the phone." A muffled noise resonates in the background. Definitely crying, but I think he's attempting to block the noise by covering the mouthpiece.

"Why?" I'm starting to lose my patience. "Rob? Hello? Why can't you tell me on the phone?" I haven't heard from him in weeks and now this. Anger swells up until he starts to weep. Well, now I feel awful. "Rob, what the hell is going on?"

I can hear him trying to catch his breath. Finally, he sputters out, "You're gonna hear some stuff about me that you're not gonna like." More sobs. "It's bad, Zette. Really bad."

"Okay, what do you mean by bad? Like, how so?"

"Please come to Chicago. Please, please come."

My heart is pounding. I've never heard him this scared. "I have a job, Robert. I can't just leave right now."

"I will pay any amount. I'll make up for it. Just come."

"I'll let you know." His pain gnaws at me, but that record deal meeting is coming up. My agents even said Rob would be the reason I didn't make it if I kept giving in. "Let me think about it, please. I just need a day."

As anyone who knows me would have guessed, a few days later, I'm being picked up in a limo at O'Hare. The second I set my things down in the hotel room, I snap up the phone and call my managers in New York. Their confusion quickly turns to frustration as I try to explain. I say Rob was crying, so I had to come. It sounds so lame saying it out loud.

"The meeting with Motown is in two days. Get back to New York, now!"

Per usual, Rob shows up late that night, but this time, he's clearly rattled. Crying and hardly making sense, his words stray off at times and practically dissolve into babbling at others. Drunk and upset aren't generally a great combination for important communication. As he starts to get his head straight, I start piecing things together. Something about a girl he claims he didn't have a relationship with and a lawsuit.

"I didn't do anything wrong... I didn't," he keeps repeating, collapsed on his knees in front of me. "Someone is bringing up lies against me. I don't know what to do." I can tell he's fucked up on something. "Please stay, Zette. Don't leave."

For the second time in twenty-four hours, I call my managers. This time, it's to tell them I don't think I can make the Motown meeting. Understandably, they're upset. The meeting can't happen without me. They remind me this is my chance—there might not be other opportunities if I back out now. My stomach twists as I repeat that I probably won't make it back in time. Ugh, another chance out the window, but what am I supposed to do? Robert is here on the freaking floor in tears. I can hear their disappointment through the phone.

"We suggest *really* thinking hard about this relationship with him. We wish the best for you, but this opportunity is not coming again. Just in case you change your mind, we'll be there waiting for you."

The second I hang up I feel like I've made a mistake. My heart aches for Rob and whatever he's going through, but I needed this. Really needed this. I turn back to the dejected man behind me, standing now. Rob paces, drinks, mutters about the unfairness of it and how it's not true. Partially to me, but also kind of just to himself. I'm sitting on the end of the bed, waiting, struggling to be consoling wherever I can. Sinking down next to me, his eyes are wide and worried, staring into the carpet at nothing. Gradually, with more swigs of alcohol, the intensity starts to leak out, replaced by crumpled defeat. We exchange words for a little bit, but he's unwilling to say much more. Then he reaches for me. Even distraught, in the middle of some legal fiasco about another woman, he reaches for me.

When he's finished, he heads off to the studio, leaving me alone in the dark.

The weekend is a torturous combination of being there for Rob emotionally and physically, then being left in the room to worry, knowing I missed my shot at a record deal. By the end of the weekend, I'm livid. He didn't need *me* that badly. He probably *needs* a lot of women comforting him right now. I leave Chicago angry at him and myself, having given up one more chance to make it on my own.

CHAPTER 17

Rob still has houses in Chicago that he owns or rents, but never puts me up in them. Instead, he swaps me around the same group of hotels. Sometimes my stay in the city is split between separate hotels, starting in one and ending in another. He keeps me away from his personal life, saying it's for my own good, to protect me.

I'm not allowed to leave the hotels without permission, sometimes not even the room. It's been this way for a while. Most times I do leave, Rob hears about it somehow. Some little bird twittering in his ear—someone sitting in the lobby probably being paid to let him know if I'm up to something. Rob starts insisting I call him "Daddy" in private and ask for permission to charge his card to eat. He knows I don't have anything else. I can't pay for it on my own.

I see young women at the hotel all the time, still at an age you can refer to them as *girls*, no parents, hanging around in expensive lobbies in Chicago. They linger, dressed up and faces painted on, clearly waiting for someone. Deep down, I know. I mean, how could I not? One day, these two Spanish girls are waiting in the lobby, must be seventeen and eighteen if I'm being extremely generous. As soon as I see them, I can feel the truth of their presence crawling up my spine. I start walking towards them, ready to ask who they're here for, but stop short and press the button for the elevator instead.

With a couple years of trekking between Chicago and New York under my belt, the O'Hare airport is routine to me now. I know where to get the better coffee, where the closest bathrooms are from the terminals, and don't have to follow the signs to get to the baggage area or the loading stations. Rolling just one smaller bag, plus the purse on my shoulder, I stroll through the glass doors to encounter hordes of slim young women with large chests squeezed into tight shirts. They're all gorgeous, excited, and I'm honestly a little confused as to why there are so many in one place. As I roam the pickup area, looking for my ride, someone taps on my shoulder.

"Hey," the stern voice comes from a guy wearing all black and a headset, holding an additional cell phone and clipboard. "We're all heading into those limos grouped right over there, if I can just check your name off so we know you're not missing. Welcome to the mansion."

"Uhhh. What?"

He looks me up and down. "Are you not here for the Playboy event?"

"Nope." I can see one of Rob's drivers waving from a limo nearby. I point. "I'm over there." Rushing over, clutching my stuff tightly, I breathe deep. Thank god I'm not here for that. Nodding at my driver, who comes around to open the door for me, I shake my head at the offer to take the small bags and set them inside on the floor as I scootch in. No Rob. Seriously? He's been asking me to come back for months. I left my job for this. Again.

Breathing deep to stay calm, I watch the city go by. And the traffic. More traffic than city. Pulling onto an exit, we swivel a bit on a mix of one-way and two-way roads and arrive at our destination. A valet opens the door and offers a hand to take my things and help me out of the limo. Grasping his hand and pressing my heel down hard to lean out and stand, I look up to see where I'm placed *this* time. The Hotel Nikko. A good spot, one of the usuals, and my friend works here, but I'm also pretty sure there's no Rob on the way to welcome me. At the front desk, I state my name and, once more, the desk agent gives me a knowing nod and repeats someone else's name as she hands me a key. It's never under Robert Kelly. Ever. Plastic key card gripped between my fingers, I stalk over to the elevator, trying to pan the area as I do so. Just in case he's here... He's not. I open my suitcase in the room, disappointed he's still nowhere to be found.

After the miscarriage, I felt broken, and as time passed and it hit harder that nothing could change my loss, something snapped in me. I don't know if I'm becoming a stronger person, attempting to negate the brokenness I feel, or finally emptying that teenage angst a million years too late, but I've started caring a lot less about Rob's rules. When someone doesn't show up for the loss of their child, *your child*, it does something to ya. Hence, my automatic stroll to the room's mini bar in his absence to see what's up.

I try calling but there's no answer, so I do a little post-flight grooming, slip on something for Rob's first glimpse, and head down the elevator to chat with the front desk.

"Any messages from Robert Kelly?"

"Um... no, my apologies, I'm not seeing anything. Were you expecting a call?"

"Possibly, but no worries." Pushing through the hotel's main glass doors, I wander over to the street corner, away from the valets, and lean against the wall to smoke. Technically, this act *alone* isn't allowed according to Rob. I "left the premises." Didn't even ask. To rub it in a little extra, I finish the cigarette entirely then saunter back in the doors and head to the bar downstairs instead of returning to my room. If he comes to see me, I won't even be up there waiting for him.

A group of Middle Eastern musicians sit clumped up at a bunch of tables that have been lazily squashed together.

They're passing smokes, chattering over each other and "cheers"-ing loudly. One of them waves me over, pulls up a chair next to him and introduces himself. Turns out he's crazy rich, as in loaded like a Saudi prince. It's a little unclear if he's with the gathered band or just happens to be here, but we talk for a while, leading him to extend a dinner invitation.

"No, sorry, I'm waiting on someone." It's a struggle to push the words out. Feels like they're coming from someone else. I can't even tell if that tone in my voice is regret or despair. Probably both. As he nods his understanding, a cold line shivers down my back and I get that feeling of someone watching me.

Since I know the spy of the day will disappear as soon as I stand up—if they were sent by Rob—I try to sip the remainder of my cocktail while directing a subtle side-eye glance around the room. There are only a couple other groups scattered about and none of them look connected to R. Kelly or his managers. No one in sports gear, chains, or dressed like a security guard. Am I at the point of real paranoia? Drifting off the charts? I'm over this bullshit. With a goodbye to the whole table, I keep my eyes sharp as I head to the elevator. That "watched" sensation raises all over my skin like beads of sweat. My finger jabs at the elevator button a couple more times. I don't care if I break a finger. I want to get upstairs.

A few hours later, the knock at the door comes. I can already tell by the aggressive knock that its bearer is not happy. Swinging open the door, a pissed-off Rob braces himself in the doorframe.

"You think I don't know what you're doing!?" As he strides in, livid, he seems to swallow up the whole space, even the air. "You think I don't know you're smoking cigarettes outside by yo'self and talking to some fuckin' old man?"

I'm backing up fast. My heel catches on the carpet.

"Think I don't have people watchin' you, Zette?"

"I was… I was just bored, Rob. You weren't here, it feels like you're never here, and I came to see you."

"I don't want to hear that shit. Thas why I don't take you serious. You hear me?"

His hands clamp around my neck and wrangle me onto the bed. Coughing and gasping, I can't see his face, it's blurred by the front area lights shining from behind. "That's why you never gonna make it, you dumb bitch. You don't listen to me."

His hands release my neck, but the rage that fills the room makes it hard to breathe. The darkness is thick, like there's weight in it. "Smoking a cigarette with some old man… You want an old man tonight, bitch?"

My feet slip on the bed's top cover as I shift myself up against the backboard. I cough and cry out, "You weren't even at the airport to pick me up. You've been asking me to come for months. Why am I here?" The second the words leave my mouth I want to pluck them back and swallow them whole. Never let them float into existence in the first place.

"I'm *busy!*" Rob screams, now a dark figure at the end of the bed. "What? You don't know I got a Grammy award now? I'm doing big things, I'm friends with famous people, and you think I have the goddamned time to pick *you* up from the airport!" My body is squeezed as close to the wall as it can get, wishing I could slip through it to a better life, leave all this behind. I press my fingers harder. The pain helps me shut out Rob's voice, whatever he's yelling about right now.

A moment of silence takes hold and I look up. He's in the main area of the suite, sitting under the lights on a chair, floor to ceiling windows beside him, looking out to the busy streets of Chicago. Hands folded like a prayer across his face, he watches me as I cry, still huddled against the wall. "Come over here," he says. I don't move. "Come over here, Zette." There's a shard of sorrow in his words, maybe apology, that prompts me to stretch my legs and push myself off the bed to walk over to him. "Good girl." He smiles. "Kneel down." He's sliding his shorts down and holding himself out to me. It's not a choice anymore. I give him head and he finishes on my face. My head dips down as Rob sighs and pushes a hand towel at me. Wiping at my cheeks, I stumble to the bathroom to shower the feelings off: the grime, the humiliation, the knowing I don't have options. I made choices, and here I am.

Freshly showered, I perch myself on the edge of the bed, still crying. I can't help it. Rob won't look at me. He drops cash on the side table and leaves without saying a word.

Since I already left my job in New York, I decide to stay. Rob comes when he wants. If he's in a mood, I have to ask permission for every single thing I do. Using the bathroom or taking a shower suddenly needs his go-ahead. Michella thinks it's silly and I should just go, but I don't want the fight that would come. Or the punishment. Every act of defiance comes with consequences, and I've been wiping my face with towels and crying myself to sleep too much lately.

If I defy the larger rules to stay within the hotel— preferably my room—when he's away, punishment comes in the form of abandonment. Rob doesn't return for a while, doesn't call, lets me wonder for days if he's going to come back at all. It's always because I left the room for food or went out on the sidewalk for a smoke, so it's not like leaving the hotel to prove a point is an option. Then he'd just be gone longer. If he stayed away long enough, I'd probably starve waiting for him. So, I hide in the room and order room service, read magazines and books, sit bored out of my mind, and watch TV. He rarely brings me to the studio anymore.

Days I'm allowed out, it's either accompanied by Robert or because he's given me money for shopping as a conciliatory present. One morning, I wake up to three thousand dollars in cash lying on the side table with a note telling me to go buy myself some new clothes. It's probably a good idea. My wardrobe consists of the few items I packed on the way to Chicago, not expecting it to turn into more than a week or two, so I repeat the same pieces over and over with adjustments.

Excitement flickers at the thought of fresh clothing and new dresses, but it plunges as soon as I picture myself entirely alone the bustle of downtown Chicago. Since no one has been able to take me anywhere, and I haven't been allowed out by myself to wander, I don't know where anything is. There's a well-known mall somewhere, but I don't know if it's a reasonable cab ride, or if I'd even end up at the right place.

Instead, I end up on Michigan Avenue in my heavily recycled outfit, which is looking a little drab, uncertain which places sell clothes I would wear. I walk around the blocks for a while, window shopping and occasionally ducking my head in a door to see something specific. When I finally find a spot I like, I go inside to examine a jacket, only to be ushered out *Pretty Woman* style. Sarcastic comments, nasty giggles at my clothing, and all. Still needing something to wear, I try a few more shops, but they all treat me the same. So much for an updated wardrobe today.

Giving up, I notice the Nike Store down the street and walk a little faster. The familiarity inside is heaven. No one is giving me strange looks or making sure I don't touch anything. After circling the interior a few times, enjoying being in a different space, I buy a T-shirt for Rob and go back to the hotel, exhausted. I set the bills back on the side table and relax in front of the TV.

A few hours later, when Rob shows up to see how it went, I hand him the T-shirt. He looks down at it.

"You didn't buy anything for you?"

I shake my head. He gives me a strange look, but then he's smiling and cuddling up next to me, then we're having sex.

Rob stops us temporarily to buy pay-per-view porn to watch on the screen while I get him off. It's been on before, but not quite this raunchy and not with an all-male cast. Maybe he secretly wants to date men. He does like toys in odd places. When it's over, and we're laying there on the bed, I try to bring it up all casual (which means I sound awkward as hell) and let him know he can tell me if he's gay or bisexual or whatever—it doesn't matter to me.

Sitting up, he looks me straight in the eyes and says, "If you think I'm gay, then I'm gay." Then he shrugs, stands up, gets dressed, and leaves with a limp handwave. The money is still sitting on the table next to me. I leave it. I don't know what to do with it.

***

I've stayed at the Marriott so often over the years, I'm friends with some of the staff. Most nights, I sit by myself downstairs in the lobby and watch Michael Jordan walk in and out on his own escapades while I wait for friends to finish their shifts. They always give me the lowdown about everyone staying in the hotel. You can learn a lot about celebrities and important figures from front desk agents. You can learn a lot more from someone who works hotel room service.

One evening, I agree to get drinks with two of the Marriott staff, a guy and a girl who both work the main lobby. They know full-well that Rob always has people watching, so we don't leave the hotel, but we seek out a spot where we know it's harder to overhear. As soon as we've semi-escaped prying ears and are settled at a secluded table with cocktails, one of them turns to me and puts a hand on my wrist.

"Lizzette, you need to know that Rob comes here with other girls. Like they're here at the hotel right now."

It shouldn't be this hard to breathe. Of course part of me has always known, so my shock is surprising in itself, but hearing it out loud is like hearing your boyfriend admit he cheated on you. You might realize it's probably happening, but it doesn't make it hurt any less when it's confirmed. I gulp my drink to fend off the tears and raise my hand for another. Not sure if it'll help, but there's nothing else I can do at the moment. Several cocktails later, I tell my friends I'm going back to the room to rest. Their pasted smiles assure me they know exactly why I'm heading up right now: to get a good and proper cry.

I push myself out of my chair, give hugs, and stumble off towards the elevator. As I'm looking around for evidence of "said girls," my eyes spot something familiar outside the front doors, by the valet station. My heels click as I strut faster, until I reach the door and rest a hand on the pristinely wiped glass. Robert's favorite car is sitting right there, the young valet just now getting inside to formally move it to the underground parking lot. Rob's definitely here at the hotel, just not with me.

Now the waterworks are legit about to start, so I swivel around and march back to the elevators. The moment I'm alone, I let myself slump in defeat. *You knew all along, didn't you?* I manage to fumble the key into the door and let myself in before I crumble to pieces. The devastation is like a vast black hole pulling at me, draining any bits of hope or happiness I'd been clinging to. Dragging myself to bed, I fall asleep with my clothes on, utterly exhausted from it all.

The longer I stay in Chicago, the more our sex life becomes a humiliating ordeal, and I wonder over and over if this is what love is supposed to be like. Is putting up with your partner's sexual kinks part of loving them or should you say no and hold your ground? And what happens if I tell him no? He would probably be upset, refuse me, and then our relationship is ruined. Over. On top of it, Rob won't wear condoms, so I pray all the time that whoever else he might be seeing is clean and healthy.

The romance in our intimacy died a while ago—if it was ever really there at all. Lately I've felt like I'm just a sex object, a doll to get pleasure out of whenever Rob pleases. I won't see him for a couple days, then he'll show up, want me to perform in some way, and maybe stay the night or maybe go to dinner, but generally he just leaves right after. The brief visits are more common when he stops by in the middle of the day. It's at the point where it's not uncommon for him to burst through the door around lunchtime, immediately take off his shorts, and make me give him head until he comes all over my face. I'm on my knees the whole time, held there by large hands. The worst part is that it's usually after he's been playing basketball. Everything is sweaty and rank, sticky before we even start.

It's not unusual for me to cry through it. Which sounds weird, right? Sometimes he's really into it and doesn't seem to want to cater to me because he'll lose his high. Other times it's because I piss him off. I think that's when he enjoys the crying, like it proves he's making his point. Those days are super rough physically. I mean, it's always rough, that's just how he is, but those stretches are hard to get through. My scalp hurts afterwards from the hair pulling.

I cry after he leaves too, so at least it's good that he splits directly after getting his relief. When he does finally walk out the door, I'm always so mad at myself. I don't want to do this stuff, but for some reason I do it anyway. I'm not sure if I'm afraid of him or losing him or if it's just ingrained in me that this is what you do for the person in your life. Maybe it's ingrained in me that you get in trouble if you say no. My childhood could testify to that. But this... this isn't how I was raised. I never would have imagined my adult relationship would include being smacked in the face with his clammy, post-workout manhood. It seems so normal to him, like he's been doing it forever. Some days when I have too much time to think, I wonder if I'm turning into someone else, something I never wanted to be. I don't feel strong enough to stand up against it. And when I do, it always ends badly for me.

One night, Rob calls up to the room from downstairs, and I'm tired, so I snap back at him when he says something mean. The line clicks off, and I assume he's going to avoid me for a few days to teach me a lesson. Nope.

Less than a minute later, he's in the room, hands around my neck, threatening to show everyone how disloyal I am. Wrenching open the door, he drags me down the hallway towards the elevator. My kicking, screaming, and crying do nothing to deter him until we're almost there. The second he loosens his grip to press the down button, I'm flinging myself down the hallway and sprinting back to the door. He runs after me, catching the door before I can slam it shut.

Within minutes, security is knocking and Rob motions for me to answer. I crack the door and peer out into the bright hallway at a large, rumpled man with a badge signifying his security status.

"Miss, are you okay?"

Rob stays hidden behind the door, but he's so close I can feel the heat of his breath on my shoulder.

"I—I'm fine." My words don't even convince *me*. To my left, Rob has a fist raised and ready. If I mess this up, I'm getting knocked upside the head the second we're alone.

"No, you're not. What's going on here?" The guard is trying to edge his way in with his bulk to get a better view of the room.

"Really, I'm fine. Please, it's okay."

His eyes are gentle as he dips his head down, "No, I think it's best if you came downstairs."

By now, I have tears streaming down my face as I beg him to please leave me alone. Silently pleading for him to please get the point. Please don't get me in trouble. The man offers a swift nod, one last concerned look, and turns back towards the elevator.

My body slouches against the door, pressing it closed from my weight, and I sink into a sobbing crouch. Rob throws me one last look and lowers his fist in slow motion directly in front of my face before walking over to the bed. I know the point he's making. He owns me.

CHAPTER 18

Every time I try to leave Rob for good, I keep coming back. The same pattern as my early days in New York return: weekends spent in Chicago, fly back to New York for work, then, every once in a while, stay with Rob for a couple weeks and call out for my job, find a new job when I get back. If I even come back.

When we fight, he leaves for days, using the pressure of the silent treatment to coax me into feeling bad enough to forgive first. I'll be angry, then flustered, then start to worry, and once I'm worrying, the doubt creeps in. By the end of the cycle, I'm practically panicking that Rob won't be back this time, and I'm alone for good. He always comes back, though, usually with a gift. He's always gentle and sweet when I see him again, and I wonder if I'm blowing everything out of proportion.

When I confess my doubts to Rob directly, he reminds me how busy he is. There isn't always time for me. He's vital to the music industry right now and where it's going. I guess it's easy to forget that he's not just Robert to everyone. Anytime he feels I've been too needy, he reminds me, asking if I remember who he is. Usually, he leaves for longer after these conversations, just to make sure the point hits home.

***

It should be a vivid fall morning in Chicago, but I wake up to irritated, oozing eyes. Between how swollen they are and the thick layer of goo sticking them together, I can't open either more than a slit. I manage to shuffle around and find clothes, dressing myself awkwardly, then call the front desk to set up a taxi to Northwestern Hospital. Once admitted to the ER, after wandering in blindly, I'm told one of my corneas is scratched and infected. The infection is already so bad it's spread to the other eye. They keep me at the hospital for two days to watch it and ensure I don't go blind or lose my eyes entirely—since apparently those are real possibilities.

A doctor explains that my contact severely scratched my cornea but asks if I've had anything unusual (possibly unsanitary) in my eyes lately, since the contact alone shouldn't have led to an infection this extreme. That... I don't answer. It might lead to other questions that would end in having to explain my relationship with Rob. I know he doesn't want that line of questioning right now. Underneath, though, unease about something this simple making me go blind permanently scrapes at me with fear.

Early on, I ask the nurses to call Robert. They leave messages and assure me he'll probably show up. He doesn't. Demetrius does instead.

"He sent you instead?" The bitterness in my voice is like cut glass.

"Lizzette," Demetrius says as he drags a chair up next to the bed, "You gotta understand. He's in his own world. Rob's an artist, and he has to own it and do his thing. You know he loves you."

"Are you serious right now?" *This is not love.*

"I don't know what to tell you, he's all about himself. You know that. I'm sorry he's not here, but I'm not gonna leave. Okay?"

To be fair, even though Demetrius covers for Rob a lot, he also tries to help him, shape him into a better person. I don't think he knows the extent of Rob's twistedness. How could he? Rob isn't sticking his junk in Demetrius' face. Demetrius is allowed to leave the hotel, use the bathroom, and eat whenever he wants. I wonder what he thinks of me, or other women he's seen stick around Rob. Does he think I like staying inside all the time? How much does he let slide and how many times does he choose to look away and not see what's happening in front of him?

True to his word, Demetrius stays by my side while I'm stuck in the hospital. When he gets updates from Rob, he tells me. They are always the same: Rob is at the studio, working on something. As soon as the nurse grants me permission to leave, I tell Demetrius exactly what I need right now to keep going.

"I want to leave, for good, but I need money to do that. Please, help get me some money so I can go. I just wanna leave. Start over." The words hardly come out I'm crying so hard. When they do, I'm stuttering enough to make my head rattle. From the way his intense expression shifts to melancholy and then a half smile, I know he hears me. He doesn't fight it, just nods and sets a hand on top of mine. In that moment, I realize he's probably been waiting for this, maybe even hoping for it. He does see what goes on, but he can't make decisions for me when I keep putting myself in the same position.

Demetrius leaves the room to call Rob, and I slip off my crumpled hospital gown to pull on my own clothing again. Doubt snakes up my spine as I fold up the gown and set it on the bed. It's the right thing to do, for me. The most important thing is taking care of myself. A deep inhale, and I pat the gown and turn to put on shoes. When a knock sounds at the door, Demetrius slowly pokes his head in.

"You're all set. I'm taking you back to the hotel to pick up your stuff and then I have to go meet Rob, so you're picking up the money from Derrel. If you have any problems, just call me. I'll keep my phone close by."

Packing my belongings doesn't take long, so I'm on the way to this random swanky hotel to pick up my "get out of here and heal" cash within an hour. I'm not sure if Demetrius discussed it with Rob in advance and settled on an amount or if he's just helping me out of his own pocket. If he did tell him, Robert is clearly angry. Rob once set three thousand dollars on my bedside table to buy pants and shirts and dresses, but now it's one thousand to recover from the last four years, a miscarriage, and a severe eye infection while restarting in another state. Maybe he knows I don't intend to come back this time. That I mean it. Either way, this is the only course I see to get home and heal, because I don't have funds after being trapped in a room on and off for so long, not being able to work.

The cab pulls up to a super glitzy hotel where two men offer slight bows on my way in. Glass doors with intricately carved golden handles are opened far in advance by a gloved hand belonging to a cheery man in a vest and bowtie. Looking around the extravagant marble lobby, I notice a couple plush chairs past the reception desk and make my way over to wait. He knows I'm coming. Within minutes, Derrel McDavid is exiting the elevator. I stand up to catch his eye and he ambles over to me in a button-up shirt, mustache twitching with a smile.

"Wow. You're looking very pretty." The wink is a little much.

"Thank you," I say, hoping my business voice sounds professional and severe enough to make this an easy and swift transaction. I want to be on my way.

He chuckles a little, probably at my clear lack of appreciation for the comment, and hands over a wad of cash. "Here you go, lovely."

"Thank you."

"Have a good day, Li—" Derrel attempts, but I'm already striding towards the door, ready to get the hell out of here and leave the life I have with Rob behind.

CHAPTER 19

Back in the glorious heat of Miami, I'm collecting myself, putting all the little pieces of my life back together. There's a weird feeling of normalcy about all of it. After all the back and forth and waiting on Rob's generosity, it's an accomplishment to stand on my own two feet. Robert knows I don't want to see him anymore.

He's tried calling.

The first attempt to reach out was an apology of sorts: "Zette? That song, "You Are Not Alone"—that song is for you. You know that situation happened, and I wasn't there, and you lost the baby, and I know you've been on your own a lot. Even as a kid. I wanted you to know that I'm thinking of you even when you're not in Chicago with me."

Missed a few more calls, then got this one: "Zette! I've found the Lord!"

"Sorry, what?"

"I found God, Zette, and I'm 'bout to head on the straight and narrow."

"Oh, cool."

"All that dark stuff I did in the past. It's gone and forgiven, and I'm done with it. I'm done doing bad things."

"I'm genuinely happy to hear that. Good for you, Rob."

"Yeah, jus' wanted you to know. I'm on a new path."

I let the next calls go. I need to finally move on and not let things linger, otherwise I get swept up again and that can't happen this time around, whether he's changed by God or not.

Then the bump shows up. It's a bump down there, looks like razor burn to me. Being the hypochondriac that I am, when it's not looking better in a day, I call my longtime primary care physician, Dr. Jacobson. It seems like overkill to strip down and brace my feet into the cold stirrups for what's possibly just an ingrown hair, but the assurance it's being taken seriously is comforting. At least it is until his Dr. Jacobson's female partner scrutinizes the area, prods it a bit, and announces she's ordering a blood test.

"Why a blood test?"

"It's most likely an STD," she casually responds.

I don't think she expects the immediate waterworks breakdown.

"It's okay. It happens," she tries to reassure me. "It's not that uncommon."

At this point, I can't hear her, really, because after all the shit that's gone down, this one extra cherry on top has set me blubbering like there's no tomorrow. I can hardly catch my breath. "How did this happen to me?"

Stepping back, she uses a very matter-of-fact voice, "Well, who have you been with?"

"Just Robert. I mean, Rob, R. Kelly."

"If he's it, then that's how you got it."

She lets me take my time getting dressed so I can compose myself before leaving. A week later, blood tests come back positive. I call Rob right away, like a responsible adult, despite how much I do not want to hear his voice right now. There's a strained silence in between each sentence as I explain the positive results and that he needs to be checked and at the very least be careful, because I haven't been with anyone else. When I'm through with my spiel, he still hasn't said anything.

"Robert, are you still there?"

"Yeah, Lizzette, I don't know how you got that 'cause I don't have that."

"Excuse m—"

"Musta been someone else, huh?"

By the time our conversation is over and I'm pressing the button to end the phone call, I'm on my floor bawling. Not just because I'm upset about having an STD, but because I feel humiliated about having it, and then humiliated again by him not owning up to it. He straight up accused me of being loose, talking to me like I was trash who's just out with anybody and could have gotten it anywhere. I haven't been with anyone. I couldn't even go to McDonalds alone or smoke a cigarette on the sidewalk, much less have a late-night tryst with a stranger.

I knew he was seeing people, tried not to think about it too much, but I knew. I was really, desperately hoping he would at the very least be safe since he was also proclaiming his love and how much he needed me all this time. *There's probably thirty girls in Chicago finding "razor bumps" right now.* I can't believe I'm one of them.

Letting myself cry it out is somewhat therapeutic. And it's there on the floor that I decide I'm going to give in to my anger. Start protecting myself from him.

***

"He's having a concert and says it's essential that you call him."

"Robert don't talk like that."

"Zette, come on girl, you know what I mean! He came into my store the other day and recognized me. All he could talk about though was you and how he needs to speak with you, blah, blah, all that stuff. Asked if I'd seen you in the last few months or if I knew how to get ahold of you."

Months I've spent trying to move past and, more importantly, away from the trauma of those nights in

Chicago. I've been staying with my mom in Miami in a little one bedroom, working and going to night classes to get the high school diploma I missed out on before. I should have foreseen a pothole like this coming, but somehow, it catches me unaware. I spend a week considering it.

"Hi... heard you were looking for me." Damn it, I gave in and called.

"Zette!" There's surprise in Rob's voice. "I miss you, you know." Of course he does. "I love you and I'm sorry."

"Wait. Listen. You did a lot of things," I say. My head is screaming, *don't cry, don't cry, keep it together.* "I'm trying to get my own life together now. You understand?"

"Right now I'm staying at the Grand Bay Hotel in Coconut Grove, can you just come over... please? I want to talk to you."

Naturally, all of my resolve washes away immediately. Also, I'm curious if the dynamic will be different now that I've spent time away. Once I've taken my sweet time getting ready, I walk to the full-length mirror, scanning my body up and down. Everything is feeling good, I'm good, and there's no reason he should be able to hurt me again. This chica is ready. Yes, that's my pep talk. And yes, it's necessary right now.

Rob kisses me in welcome when I first enter the room, but my motivational speech in the mirror must have worked because I stay strong through the entire conversation between us. My head is clear, my attitude respectfully nonchalant, I think I've got this, and then he invites me to his concert the next night. This... throws me off. Not exactly on par with the fix-up-my-life plans. Also, I'm not big on watching overdramatic fans drool over Rob.

Initially I say I'll think about it, but agree to go when Nicole offers to join me. I'm uncertain about the whole post-concert part of the night. Not sure what exactly my responses should be yet if I'm being independent and true to myself. Still, I try to enjoy the moment, stay chill, listen as though it's just music. Just another concert.

The voices of these girls behind us butt into my attempt at zen thoughts.

"I met him last night!"

"Oh shit, really?"

"Yeah, we got close." Laughter. They're pushing and pulling at each other's shoulders, snickering and rocking back and forth. "Girl, of course I did! He invited us back tonight. Why you think I'm here?"

I shake my head slightly. Up to the same old shit.

The concert experience itself is awkward because he's singing all the songs I was there for, either playing around or giving feedback as he wrote them. Can't quite shout out, *Heard these before, can we move forward? Too many memories associated here.* On the other hand, not a huge fan of going down this particular memory trail.

Nicole and I look at each other. She gives me an empathetic smile, "What do you wanna do?"

With a groan, I admit, "I don't know. He invited John and everyone to an after party." My eyes are focusing on a group in front of me, trying to push the shrieky voices of the girls from earlier out of my head. Maybe if I squint hard enough.

"Me and him are friends. I really want to go, but I get it if you don't." She's so nice.

My squinting moves to the lights. I know I'm avoiding making a decision. I can zone out if I stare into the brightness, it'll at least get rid of those girls' faces. Without fully realizing it, I respond, "That's okay. I guess we can go or whatever."

Just like my first concert, there is no going backstage after the concert for me. The girls behind us are probably back there right now, and I have zero interest in watching them fawn over him. Honestly, the idea makes me sick. Besides, I've already been everywhere in private with him. At this point, going backstage is a groupie charade.

When we get outside, I call, and Rob tells us to meet him back at the hotel if we're not headed backstage. He'll send people to drop by and take us to the party once they're on their way. Since this time around I don't have a key, he says Demetrius can let us in the room to wait.

As it's the same hotel I just met him at yesterday, I immediately head up towards the room from the other night. Luckily, Demetrius intercepts us along the way, saying no, Rob's got another room for us to wait in until he can stop by or send someone over. Guiding the way, Demetrius unlocks the door while we huddle outside a room on a floor I've never stayed in before, unusual for Rob, then he waves us inside.

It's been hours. Rob hasn't showed, hasn't called, and no one has arrived to accompany us to the afterparty. The sting isn't supposed to be this bad when you're letting go. I'm moving forward, and don't need this kind of uncertainty in my life. That's about as far as my self-reassurance goes. Nicole has to leave because she's currently taking care of her parents while they're in a transition period. I don't have a way home, and my mom would be pissed if I knocked on the door to be let in at five a.m. or something ridiculous that would wake her up in the dead of night.

Waiting is looking like my best bet, even if it's solo for a while. Definitely looks like no one will be picking me up to join the party, which isn't so bad. I didn't really want to go to that anyway. I wonder briefly if Rob even remembers that I'm waiting for him here, in this random room that is not the room he was staying in the other night for our reunion chat.

If he's not coming, I'll just stay here tonight and figure it out in the morning. There's not much else to do.

Tears start rolling down hot and fast as I sit on the corner of the hotel bed. Swiping my eyes with the backs of my hands, I fold the top comforter down to lay back on the sheets, defeated tears leaving dark spots on the soft cream fabric. This has happened a million times before. It always makes me upset, but not like this. The same injured heart that cried for her lost baby is now crying at being abandoned after trusting this person I keep trying to love, this one last time. I can't continue hurting myself like this. I need to be over it, completely over it.

My breathing slows, and I finally lull into an unthinking grey zone that drifts into a light, fitful sleep. If I can be unconscious, I can at least make it to tomorrow without being hurt any further.

I am a damn fool.

There are so many wonderful things about fancy hotels. The food is delicious, room service is great, beds are lusciously squishy and packed with pillows, the bars are splendid and offer top-shelf cocktails at exorbitant prices. Another endearing aspect of upscale hotels is they tend to be fairly quiet. Unless you're in a suite that shares a door, the walls are thicker, there's more space between rooms, and people literally paid more for better rest. You can't generally hear much unless there's drunk guests arguing in the hall, tiny screaming children nearby, or they're having a full out party next door.

Screaming children do not wake me up from the other side of the shared, bolted door, but a woman's high-pitched voice does. Music reverberates against the walls and shattering laughter pierces the nighttime silence. It's still insanely early, and I can hear the heavy door in the room next to mine opening and slamming shut.

You know how when you've really been with someone for a while, you know their quirks, right? You know how their eyes scrunch when they laugh, or what their night breathing sounds like, or how they clutch their wine glass when they're thinking. You recognize their real laugh and their fake one, the throat clear that means they want to leave soon please and the please-introduce-me one.

The door to the next room slams again and I hear Rob clear his throat and laugh. Too many nights together to not be absolutely sure of that sound. Everything inside me freezes. It's like swallowing mud. All these emotions sit heavy in my chest and stomach. Turning to my purse, I extract my phone from the mess of lipstick, bobby pins, and random receipts, and call Nicole. It's so late, it's not even fair to be calling now, but she answers.

"Hello? Is this Lizzette? Are you okay?"

My voice hardly squeaks out an audible response, "Yeah." Slightly clearer, "Yeah, it is."

"What's going on, and what happened? Is Rob there with you?"

With a deep inhale, I press back the tears, the frustration, everything. Not because I care what she thinks, but because she needs to at least be able to understand what I'm saying. "Um, yeah... uh kind of. Rob, he... it's stupid... I mean, he's next door fucking some other girls."

"What!?"

I can hardly breathe.

"How do you know?"

This actually makes me laugh. A sad, throaty laugh muffled by hours of crying. "Please, come on."

"Zette, you gotta check. Can't just be making assumptions."

Glancing around me, I steer myself to the bathroom and pick up one of the water glasses set beside the sink, tossing the wrapper in the trash. Back at the wall, I press the cup against it with my ear against the glass bottom. It's him. His laugh breaks through the music and his voice, though unintelligible, is undeniably his. From the tone, I can tell he's cracking jokes and the girls are eating it up. The noises shift quickly from laughter and giggles to moans and squeals.

I drop the phone and cry and cry and cry. It's not about the girls. It's really not. Obviously, there were always girls. I knew. But crumpled against the wall, listening to Robert with someone else is a different story. Hearing about your husband or boyfriend cheating on you is all up to your imagination; it's different when you're standing outside his office hearing the breathy cries. Those noises go straight through you.

I forget Nicole is even on the phone, but her voice finally reaches me. "Go knock on their door!" She can't see me, but I'm shaking my head, my throat too tight to speak. "Do it!"

Pressing one palm against the wall, I push myself up and stagger to the entry door, turn the handle carefully, and push it open. I'm standing half in and half out of my room, still sniffling, trying to compel myself to work up the nerve to go hammer on their door. I can't.

I'm saved the effort of trying when it opens all on its own. Out stumbles Rob, white pants unzipped and pushed partly down. His drunk face confused but dumbly gleeful. The same face he was making the night I lost my virginity, after sniffing his way through the bathroom to energize. He only glances at me before stumbling back into the darkness behind him, where a naked woman appears briefly to slam the door shut. I go back into my room.

The knock at the door twenty minutes later drives a shiver up my back, but I open it anyway. Rob comes in crying, falling on his knees to beg for forgiveness.

Rage blows heat through my entire body, my head pounding with it. "I'm done with you," I tell him. He shakes his head, still on the ground.

"No, Zette, I want to be with you. We can get a house, get married. It can still happen."

"I can't do it anymore. I can't. I don't believe you. We didn't even have to be together tonight, you just needed to not fuck it up by lying to me. You're having sex with so many girls, you're going to get me fucking sick! You already have." It's hard to get the words out. "I'm not waiting around for you to get me sick for real."

Still on the ground looking up at me, he says, "No, you can, you can stay in Chicago with me. You'll be my…"

"Your what? Your what, Rob?"

"Zette, please."

"You asked me once before to live in Chicago with you. I went. Look what happened. Look at what you did. That's why we're here, right now." He's groaning, holding his stomach like it hurts. "You always want me there for you, but you also always want to be with your friends. I lost mine. What else do I have at this point? My music career? Ha, that's a laugh. How do I get my life back at this point?" Pulling my legs out of reach of his groping hands, I say, "I'm leaving."

"No, please don't go. Please."

"I don't even know if you'll remember this tomorrow." No stopping. I strut to the door, fling it open, and I'm gone. My face must look a wreck—makeup streaming everywhere, nose wet, eyes swollen. Pushing through the glass lobby doors, I see cabs lined up with cabbies leaning against the yellow frames, cigarettes in hand. It must be five in the morning. Still dark. One particularly patient and kind driver doesn't seem as afraid of my current emotional state as the others and opens the door for me when I beg him to take me to my mother's house. As I click the door shut, Rob appears out front, stumbling his way out of the lobby, eyes a little wild, clearly still messed up.

"I don't have any money, but you see him? You know who that is right?" I point at Robert. The driver nods. "I need to get away from him." As Rob staggers towards us, the cabbie shoots off like a dart. I'm on my way home.

My mom must recognize the look on my face as she opens the door, because there's no scolding for knocking this late; instead, she comforts me. I sleep the whole next day. When I continue sleeping into the next several days and can hardly get up, we realize something isn't right. I call my dad who picks me up and takes me to the hospital.

Doctors show me charts and test results, saying my white blood cell count is really high. They prescribe an antibiotic and tell me to stay in bed for fourteen days, and if I don't, they'll sign me in to the hospital to make sure I rest.

Not wanting to end up in the hospital, I stay in my mom's living room on her couch, watching television and hardly moving. When the news breaks that R. Kelly is canceling his next few shows, I call Demetrius in a panic. If Rob gave me something…

"Hey, it's Lizzette. What's going on with Rob? Heard he's out for a bit."

"He's just not feeling well." His voice is clipped, distracted.

"Yeah, I saw him recently, and I'm not doing well either. Any idea what he's sick with?"

"Not sure. I'm sorry, Lizette, I don't know what to tell you."

Days go by and instead of improving, my condition is getting worse. Meanwhile my head is running a replay of *I can't be sick right now,* over and over. I actually have a job and I'm working on life. This can't be now. I plead with myself to stand up, tough through it. Stand up and get back to work. It's just a matter of will.

I can't afford to lose my income right now, but I take the antibiotic for the full fourteen days before attempting a work shift. It does not go well. As soon as I'm up and trying to perform my usual tasks, the energy drains away and I start feeling severely sick again, almost passing out at work. In the morning, after a solid ten hours or so of sleep, my dad picks me up to visit a store at the mall. It's his gesture to make me feel better with everything happening lately. An attempt at normalcy after a grating two weeks. Relieved to experience a more typical day outside of bed, I relish the shower and the act of getting ready for something, even if it's tiring.

Walking through the mall together, I suddenly stumble on the tiles and nearly wipe out entirely. I pause, staring at my feet. "Dad, my toes are numb. I can't feel anything."

"It's those shoes you're wearing." He points at my wedges. "You need to stop wearing high heels all the time."

"No, no, something is wrong." There is just dead weight beneath me, with polished nails. He could be stepping on my foot and I wouldn't be able to tell.

Holding my arm, my dad helps me out of the mall and into the car, taking me back to my mom's house to rest. The next morning, I wake up struggling to breathe. Even sitting down, propped up appropriately for ideal chest expansion, I'm short of breath. My dad is working right now and my mom can't handle hospitals, so I dial a friend's number. Despite gasping through the call, she gets the gist and soon is barging through the front door to take me to Parkway Hospital. I'm seen for the breathing issues but released soon after. They ignore my recent need for antibiotics and my lifeless feet.

When my face begins to go numb and I start losing the ability to move my mouth altogether, my friend takes me in again. I'm admitted to the ER, but we hit an unexpected wall. "Is there anything psychologically wrong with Lizzette?" a doctor asks her. Ignoring the extreme exhaustion, white blood cell count, breathing issues, limb numbness, etc., they focus instead on the numb face as a side effect of anxiety.

She glares at them. "You need to admit her overnight."

Instead, they send me home. I immediately call Rob again. This time, I'm more direct.

"I don't feel well. At all. Rob, please, I think I'm gonna die. Do you know what's happening to me?" I'm crying and can hardly move my mouth to shape the words. I can taste my salty teardrops since my lips don't close entirely. Each vowel and consonant takes effort. Each breath takes effort. And now my feet are now entirely numb and useless, so I can't even leave the couch to pee without help.

"Yeah, I don't feel great either," he responds.

"But I think this is serious. Before they said it might be mono, but I already took antibiotics and it's worse all the time."

"Yeah, I already had that a while ago. Can't be."

"Rob, I can hardly move."

"Then go tell your mother, your drunk mother, to take you to the hospital again." *Heavy click.*

My mom hovers, but she won't take me to the emergency room. It's too much for her; there's past trauma. Instead, she's a helpful shadow that comes in and out to make sure there's soup, water, temperatures taken, and that I'm still alive. She dials the phone for me so I can talk to my father.

"Daddy?" It's hard to move my mouth, my cheeks feel stuck. "Daddy, ah... ah can't breathe."

"I'm coming to get you."

My father is not a big man, but when he rushes into the house, he takes one look, picks me up like a tiny child, and carries me out to the car. We head to Joe DiMaggio Hospital where, upon arrival, it doesn't take much for the nurses to realize it's dire. Maybe it's the whole my-face-doesn't-work part, but this time I'm admitted to the ER right away. Once I'm hooked up with fluids and medicine, the doctor goes out to reassure my father that I'm stabilized for the moment.

"It's a good thing you got her here right away," the doctor carries on as he flips through my records. "If you hadn't brought your daughter in within the next couple hours, she would've died in that house. We have her scheduled to see a neurologist as soon as possible."

Neurological tests reveal I've developed Guillain-Barre syndrome, triggered by the mononucleosis. My immune system is attacking my nerve cells, causing muscle weakness and numbness, which is quickly turning to paralysis. My body isn't responding well, especially after so much time spent untreated.

The neurologist pulls my dad aside in the hallway.

"I'm really sorry to tell you this, but your daughter is not going to make it. We'll do everything we can, but you should start letting the people who care know it might be their last opportunity to see her."

"How long?"

"Not long. I'm sorry to say this, but I recommend putting funeral preparations in order soon."

My father breaks down, hand against the wall, knees sinking to the tile.

I pass long days in the hospital just conscious enough to know this will be my deathbed. Everyone else knows too. Looking into my father's eyes, I can tell he's mentally preparing to lose me, to box up his emotions in order to cope. Unbeknownst to me, when he leaves, he's scrambling to get everything properly set up for when the time comes.

Dazed and exhausted beyond belief, responding whatsoever takes too much effort. Hardly aware of my surroundings, there's no reassurance to provide on my part. My grandfather and grandmother take a combination of three buses to visit me, pray over me, and sit with my dad. Grandma rocks constantly on her knees in the middle of the room, repeating the rosary over and over. Her voice sounds distant, but it's comforting all the same. The chanting sounds like a song lilting as I drift in and out. The nurses call my mom repeatedly, but she refuses to come. My dad calls her too.

"Can you please just bring some pajamas from home? She'll be more comfortable if she's not in a hospital gown. We're only trying to make her comfortable. Please."

Rob calls my mom's place where no one answers, so he calls my dad's, and my stepsister Luisa picks up.

"Hey, is Lizzette okay?"

"My sister's almost dead you asshole! Where are you? She's in the ICU after seeing *your* stupid face. She's at Joe DiMaggio hospital; if you ever care about anyone other than yourself, go see her."

That conversation doesn't last long. We don't get any calls from Rob at the hospital.

Against all odds, I start to recover. The hospital discharges me after two and a half weeks in the ICU, and I'm allowed to go home. This time, my dad brings me to his place to recover. He tells me neither he nor my mother want me talking to Robert ever again. No one heard from him since the one phone call, but he sent a check to my mom, who forwarded it on for me. A thousand dollars. One grand for nearly dying. Hell, it might be one grand for thinking I was dead. That's what my life is worth. My parents want me to sue him, call the police, and press charges.

When Rob finally does chat with my dad, they figure something out, but I can't imagine what is said to Rob. He won't tell me. Neither of them. Soon after, Rob calls me to say I'm going to be okay, that he sent my mom money. I tell him I know. As though a thousand dollars would have taken care of multiple ER and doctor visits, neurological testing, antibiotics, and weeks in the ICU. Lucky for me, my dad is a paramedic and still has me on his insurance. I'm not walking away with crushing debt, but I've got nothing. I don't have my health, a job, any kind of certainty about the future, and all my stuff is in New York still.

I buy a bed with a portion of the hush money and we put it in my dad's house instead of my mom's, just in case hospital visits are necessary again. I still need help with basic things. Being released doesn't mean healed. By the time they started treating me appropriately, my nervous system was shutting down, my limbs and face were partially paralyzed, and my feet entirely so. Now physical, occupational, and speech therapy happen a few times a week.

I need assistance to use the bathroom, where I specifically refuse to look at myself in the mirror. It's devastating. Every time I do, I see a slack face I have no control over, and I start to cry so hard it hurts my aching body. Don't want anyone to see me like this. Not even me. I ask myself a lot if this is real life. I know it is, simply 'cause it doesn't just go away with wishing or hope.

I can't lift a fork to my mouth yet. Can't control my bladder. Forget about using fingers to hold anything. I have to relearn *everything*. I have to learn how to walk again, how to stand, how to speak. I'm too frightened to ask my therapist if I'll be able to sing again, much less with the same range and tone. One simple virus and I almost left the earth altogether. One silly welcome kiss in a hotel room and I may lose everything I've worked so hard for.

CHAPTER 20

Recovery trudges slowly along. It's a relief to be around my dad more, but my stepmom resents my presence, especially since my current disabilities are attention- and time-consuming. Even as I start to heal enough to contribute to the household, my stepmother and I continue not getting along (understatement of the year), and life gradually becomes rough on everyone in the house. It's like Cinderella come to life: stepmother who doesn't want me, stepsister who can do no wrong, and it's my job to clean up the house the second I can move enough to do it without passing out.

It only takes so long to reach a snapping point. Tired of my stepmom being cruel and my stepsister rummaging through my things to "borrow" them, weeks of built-up frustration break over a backpack. A Donna Karan backpack to be specific. Leaving Rob behind in Chicago, I left nearly all my things in New York to seek Miami sunshine refuge in a rush. Everything I own I carried back with me, and it's not much. When my backpack is missing from my room and found slung over my stepsister's shoulders, everything tumbles out in a rage all at once.

I don't have the energy for a proper soapbox moment, but I point out that I've been sick and I'm still sick, I'm tired all the time, I'm done asking for respect, and I'm not gonna clean up after everyone. No way will I continue letting myself be treated terribly by someone who claims to love my father and is supposed to be family.

Not to be outdone, my stepmom gets in my face and straight screams that I have to leave. Stepping back, I turn to my father and say, "Daddy, I have to go now." I pack up what little I have, minus my brand-new mattress (which pains me a bit), tell Luisa to hand over the backpack, and head to my Catholic Grandma Felicia's crowded home. Grandma Felicia is a saint. Her house is always available, and her hands are always ready to tend to the unfortunately less loved or less successful on the family tree. Anyone going through a hard time knows they will be welcomed with open arms. This does mean that her place is often packed with relatives in need and makes for a chaotic home base, so I pick up a job as fast as possible, fighting fatigue every step of the way, at Cedar's Hospital in Miami receiving labs for testing. My first major goal: my own place. In a short couple months, life is looking up in a sweet little apartment paid for by saving up paychecks. I have my own car to get around, and man does it feel good to be working again and putting a life together.

Until the blasted phone call comes, because… of course it does.

Those damn phone calls. It always comes down to one damn phone call. One tiny speck of connection that throws you off your routine.

My close friend Ria is dating Rob's cousin, Mack, and the two moved up to Chicago together a couple years ago. She calls with the good news that she's pregnant and asks if I can come to the baby shower. This is not the upsetting phone call; this is a fabulous phone call. I'm thrilled for her and excited to be financially stable enough to pay my way for a mini trip to Chicago after everything that's happened over the last few years.

Naturally, when I arrive, she's one of those beautiful, glowing pregnant women that no one can get enough of. The time spent together is light-hearted and being away from Miami for a bit is like taking a gulp of fresh air. It feels like it's been forever.

The phone call that upsets me is the one that comes on the last day of my trip. The phone is being held out to me, with Rob waiting on the other end. I stare at the phone as though Mack is holding a slug. "I don't want to. I don't want to talk to him."

"Come on. It's one conversation. We didn't tell you before, but he's been trying to get ahold of you." He sighs at my glare. "Please, it's his last opportunity knowing where you are, since you leave tomorrow."

"Fine." I take the phone and walk as far away as the cord lets me. "Hi, how are you."

Rob's voice is eager, "I'm alright. Are you... are you feeling better?"

Please let my anger and annoyance be unmistakable in my voice, despite the nerves.

"Much better. Thanks for finally asking. Why does it matter?"

"Oh, uh, because I'm in Atlantic City and I'm heading back to Chicago tomorrow, if—well, if you wanted to stay." A laugh almost bursts out. Seriously? Now, after all this and me nearly dying in the hospital, he's asking me to not return to work and extend my vacation so we can visit. "Please just wait there for me, Zette. Please."

"Mmmmm, nope. I already got a new life. I can't see you anymore. I'm sorry." In my head, I'm screaming at him, *You kill me in every way possible with your up and down and leave and come back and everything else you do to me!*

On the other end, Rob's tone is getting frantic. Asking turns into begging turns into absolute pleading in a matter of seconds. "Please, I'll pay you to live here. You won't have to work."

"Excuse me? I have a nice job. I don't need you and I don't need to be a star anymore. I want a normal life."

"Please, just wait." There's a crack in his voice. "I'll, I'll get you out of there. I'll take you wherever you want to go."

"No." I hang the phone up myself so no one can convince me otherwise and leave the room quickly. True to my word, the next day I'm on a plane back to Miami, thinking I've finally found my resolve. I can say no to him after all.

Turns out that doesn't last. He knows he opened a door.

Rob continues calling their house after the baby shower, until I agree they can pass along my number. Then he calls me relentlessly. A month later when it comes up again, I ask my friend Nicole to come with me. Strength in numbers, right? It's just a vacation. One little visit. A free trip to Chicago—that's what I tell myself. And I don't want to go alone.

Nicole follows me through my eerily familiar flight routine and memorized O'Hare walk out to the waiting limo. I long ago stopped expecting Rob to pick me up, regardless of the begging level it takes for me to come. The drive is nicer with another person, and we're at the hotel sooner than I think.

Once again, I'm in a beautiful room. Large windows look out on the city, a spacious main area leads to two bedrooms and an expansive bathroom with an extravagant shower meant to feel like "rainwater." We drink a bit from the mini bar as we chat, and it's a refreshing contrast to my final hotel days of times before when I started downing anything present while shut up in the room by myself.

As Rob arrives and walks into the room to find us happily sipping drinks, I immediately see it all over his face.

He wants Nicole too. First, he flirts, then he pushes, then he guilts.

"Look at this nice hotel I got for you two. You gonna be cold to me? After all this?" He spreads his arms out to indicate his generosity. His smile is large and wide, it should seem exceptionally welcoming, but it feels predatory instead. Clearly caught off guard, Nicole is backing up, looking at me for help, eyes wide. In response, Rob grabs me by the arm and pulls me into the main bedroom. Pushing me down on my knees, he stares at her as he uses my mouth. Standing to the side, rubbing her arms nervously, she repeats over and over, "I don't wanna do nothing." Done with me, he pushes me back slightly and grabs Nicole.

"Come on. Look at everything I gave you two. I paid for all of it, and there can be more." His words all blend together, ringing in my ears. It's all the same, like something out of a nightmare, a guilt trip that's quickly becoming a threat. She slowly sinks to her knees as his hands slide over her shoulders, and she focuses on me for a second, eyes wide. I don't know what to do. My brain is in shock. The ringing in my ears is now deafening, like clashing cymbals. My head throbs.

What if he gets angry like he used to? What if it's worse now if I try to stop him? I feel like I'm seventeen again, helpless. One of his hands deftly turns her head back towards him; he's holding himself with the other. Robert wants head from two girls and he's going to get it. He already decided.

The guilt flows like burning waves coursing through me. I can't believe I put her in this position. My head feels like it's splitting down the middle. When he finishes on her, I can't even watch. We don't stay after that. I don't know how to fix this.

CHAPTER 21

Dragging a friend down into the twisted mess of my life chips at the already present cracks in my spirit. Returning to Miami for good, I pour myself into finding steady work, moving on entirely, and letting go of the past. All of it. No more answering the phone for more chances. Everything with Rob has to be over.

Picking myself up from my former life comes with strings of its own. It was all I knew. I'd been seventeen when it started—still a kid. Sure, you hope for fairytale love or committed, ordinary marriage, but what happens when you've been conditioned to someone else being steadily in control? Someone else taking the lead with punishment for rebellion followed by extreme acts of affection for a devotion that never makes you think twice? Welcome to the story, Craig.

I met Craig in high school. A friend of a friend, three years older, and living on his own off his parents' wealth. We stayed friends through a lot of the madness and my back and forth between cities. Enamored with me early on, he tried everything he could to get me away from Robert. Probably both for my own good *and* his, to be honest. When I moved to New York after graduation, he showed up in the city, begging me to return to Miami with him and leave Robert behind.

I remember leaning against a train window, New York fog coating the buildings and trees. Seated next to me, Craig has been trying to bring up this conversation forever, and I find the dull grey outside far more welcome than his words.

"That guy doesn't love you."

I try not to look at him. The truth is like deep water underneath you. You know it's there, but as long as you keep paddling along, you can pretend it isn't. I wish I could jump into that sea of mist rushing past the window, right now, and float away from here, from this.

"You're just a prostitute to him, Lissie." Each word pelts me like a rock. The sting makes my eyes water, so the view outside the window becomes a blurry wash of dirty grey. "Will you come to Miami, please? Come back with me." I can't look at him.

My mind wanders to the day my mom threw me out. Craig was there, solid, understanding, lumbering around picking up the garbage bags off the ratty lawn after my mother tossed all my belongings in them and dumped the tied-off plastic bags in the yard. Craig picked me up the same way he'd picked up the bags, never questioning, never complaining, just doing what he felt was good for me. I still can't say yes to him, though, so I say no.

***

When I return, broken, to Miami, I eventually run into Craig through long-time mutual friends. It's been years and the sight of him stuns me. He's reinvented himself, lost weight, created this whole new confident vibe that's fun to be around. I know as the love of his younger life, I broke his heart years before, but he's so good to me even now, it feels like none of it ever happened. His attention is present and sweet and all he seems to want is to be with me and around me. After being left in solitude in hotel rooms for so long, my loneliness happily laps up the affection.

It's incredible. There's someone there for me again. Someone who cares about my eating habits, how my dress fits, which colors bring out my eyes, and who offers advice on their favorite looks. The validation is refreshing. Being cared for again is filling so many holes after feeling so drained. Craig buys me new clothes, makes sure I'm eating healthy, and offers poignant reminders when I fall into old, unhealthy routines. All our time is spent together. I'm delightfully coddled through all of it, and I quickly (emphasis on the quick) move in with him at the house his parents provide. It feels like I'm running breathlessly into a new life headlong. For the first time in years, my decisions don't revolve around Rob, and this alone feels like an accomplishment. I let Rob drift to the back of my mind so I can keep taking in this new existence without reservations.

With renewed energy, I start working again. The first job turns out to be too much of a commute, so I switch to a position at a nursing home where I'm needed all day. It's long hours, but I enjoy the work. After giving up the prospect of my own money for so long between New York and Chicago, it's empowering to say I'm earning something for myself now. Craig isn't a huge fan of me being away all day, but I'm relieved to be out and about instead of shut in alone. In the evenings, I come home to cozy up with him on the couch, and before I know it, I'm married. Immediately, it seems, I'm pregnant for the second time in my life. It's somewhat of a shock to me, since I've been super careful.

But I like my life right now. I don't want it to change. Staring at the kitchen table, I try to brainstorm ways through this. I hide it from parents, but they find out anyway. My mother gets straight to the point, "You've got to have an abortion if you're not ready."

"I don't believe in them."

"Then it looks like you're raising babies with this man, Lissie." Raising an eyebrow, she picks up her glass of wine and heads to the porch.

Life doesn't just change because of the mornings spent slumped on the bathroom floor or the weird craving combinations that stress out my husband. Life changes because Craig changes. We go on a cruise meant to relax and appreciate the good life, but his altered mood is hard to ignore in the supposedly restful atmosphere. Instead of enjoying each other, he's starting to get snappy, pushy, kind of mean. Occasionally I catch him talking up random women on the deck or at the bar. When I don't follow his lead on what to eat or wear or do, it's an argument, the silent treatment, or being left alone in the room altogether with a warning to only come out when I'm ready to be agreeable.

Am I being rebellious due to new motherly instincts or was our relationship always like this? The uncertainty eats at me. Sitting on the deck, lost in thoughts, it dawns on me that I've let Craig guide my everyday life for a while now. It doesn't seem to me like I'm really being so different, though. Maybe it's the pressure of the coming baby, and a new focus for me. By the time we leave the cruise ship, things are bad.

Craig has started hitting me when he's upset, doesn't matter where on my body, doesn't matter that I'm pregnant. I keep working, my only relief from the tension, while he stays home. His family regularly deposits money into his accounts. Sharing with me becomes scarce. After waiting in hotel rooms for Rob to feed me before I starved, I decided I never wanted to be stuck in that situation again. So even though I'm living in Craig's place, I keep a private stash. Not all of it, so he won't get suspicious. A "rainy day" horde of bills in case everything goes wrong.

The birth of two beautiful twins is a welcome distraction from all the shit going on. A perfect pair: a boy and a girl. We carry them gently home from the hospital, settle them in fresh cribs, carefully close the door to their room, and Craig beats me silly. All I can think is, "Childbirth hurt more… at least." When he tires of hitting me, he screams, mocks, anything he can think of to bring me down. I squat on the floor, holding my stomach, still loose from pregnancy, still sore from popping out two babies in the last forty-eight hours. Over and over, I tell myself not to black out. Who knows what would happen if I did?

***

It's 2001, the twins are old enough to start showing their unique personalities, and the abuse from my husband is escalating fast. Continuing to work while managing infant twins is rough, but I know I will need to get them out of the situation at some point. Not to mention the approaching need to get *me* out of this at some point. Between working and working more, saving and putting away as much possible—not sure how Craig is making his extra funds, but they seem to be limitless—I manage to buy a townhouse in Miami on a street called Ives Dairy Road. It's solely in my name, a huge accomplishment for me, but we move into the new place together.

The summer heat brings depression with it. There isn't enough time to have my own career anymore, so days are spent inside, missing the outside world from the window and taking care of the babies without any real break. Like many new mothers, the zero-relief aspect is draining me, and who knows where Craig goes anymore. He leaves and returns randomly. Just like with Robert, I know there are other women. I know I should get out of it. Fear is my constant companion and cage.

Craig's longtime friend, Karima, becomes my closest confidant since being back in Miami—she keeps me relatively sane during this rollercoaster relationship. One day she surprises me by asking if I want to go to Cameo, where we partied as underage teens with our fake IDs.

Apparently, there's a big event happening with lots of the people we used to know. The opportunity to feel like old times again? Don't want to miss out on that. I'm dying to go, but it means convincing Craig to stay in and watch the kids. Not an easy task.

The "discord" has only gotten worse. Last month, he punched me in the face while we were driving, for "talking back." As he put it: "I'm gonna clip your wings, Lizzette." Thankfully, my face has healed enough that a few swabs of makeup can make it disappear for a single outing.

Forced to beg before he gives in, the trade of me going out is giving Craig a foot job. My body shudders at the request and I flinch, but he's not looking at me, he's too involved in the TV. His weird-ass sexual tastes, plus the abuse, has pushed me to the point where I hate touching him whatsoever, but there's no other way. I don't wanna get beat; I just healed. *This is your night! Block it out of your head later.*

Silently celebrating, I pull on a brand-new outfit. It's my post-baby-weight outfit I've been looking forward to: black leather pants, halter top, and black heels. My body looks young and tiny again from caring for the twins (nobody ever believes they're mine, they think I'm the nanny when I take them out in the double stroller), my hair flows past my breasts, framing my chest, and it's the first night I've been excited in a long time.

Staring in the mirror, I take one step forward and lightly place my hand on the glass. I can't stop looking into my own eyes. I can see it in them—dying inside. They know. I fell into the same relationship. I leave before I get upset and punch the mirror or ruin my makeup with tears. Or both.

When Karima and I arrive at the club, we dance for a bit before managing to squeeze into the VIP section, taking a seat to watch the party. Karima's rubbing her feet and complaining about how they're already hurting when she notices we're sitting next to Queen Latifah. Not even taking her hand off her foot, she smiles and calls out, "'Ey, Queen!'" then continues her ankle massage as she turns back to me. "Dumb heels."

"Suck it up, girl," I tell her, "I had to put in effort to get this night off." Her eyes get sad and I look away. "Karima, please, I want to stay for a while. I need it." She nods, and we stay. It's a big weekend in Miami. All the celebs are in town for the *How Can I Be Down? Urban Music Conference*. Recognizable, famous faces are packing into bar tops and dance floors everywhere.

Taking advantage of being able to have one recklessly happy night, I dance, get tipsy, and soak up the energetic vibes of the partygoers around me. By the time 1:30 in the morning hits, Karima is insisting we leave. Sore feet switched to dead-painful feet, and shots aren't helping enough anymore.

We exit Cameo's doors just as a large tour bus pulls right in front of the club, blocking our way across the street. Everything flashes hot and cold and my feet stall. They won't move. *Move feet!*

"Karima…" I say, "it's Rob. That's his tour bus." My voice is shaking.

"Come on. You're being paranoid. It is not."

"Yes, it is."

Just as the last words leave my mouth, a few guys hop out the side door, followed by Mack, and then *him*. R. Kelly steps off the bus, straightening his outfit and glancing around, keeping that suave demeanor goin' the whole time. He's dressed in black with diamonds all over, flashing in the distant club lights that filter through the windows. There are people between us, but he catches my eye and, unexpectedly, starts to yell.

"Zette! Oh my god, look! Mack! Look who it is."

My heart nearly stops. Turning my head slightly, I make eye contact with Karima as I fight off tears, trying to tell her

I can't move my feet to get the hell outta here. I don't wanna cry right now.

Rob pushes through the pedestrians and takes my hand. "Let's go... c'mon, Zette, let's go." I don't budge, so he moves closer. "I made a mistake. I know. I married the wrong person."

I'm frozen. I can only look at him, silent. There's too much in my head, too much in my heart, everything is bubbling up and I just want to scream, *Help me! I had twins and I'm being abused... get me away from my husband. Please. Get me a lawyer. Help. I married the wrong person.* But everything is caught in my throat. No words come out, just tears. Rob's hand is wrapped around mine like he's never gonna let go, and he's looking into my eyes the way he used to in the early days. Like he can solve everything, give me hope. Breath shuddering, all I force out is, "I... I can't." I don't even know if I'm saying it directly to him or the whole freaking world right now.

As people start to notice him and gravitate towards us like annoying flies to light, a crowd starts to form. I hear his bodyguard shouting, "Rob, we gotta go!" People are swarming in, hot and thick, and suddenly his hand isn't holding mine anymore and my stomach is dropping a million miles an hour, down through my feet, the sidewalk, the earth.

Help.

Karima grabs my hand and rushes me off to the side of the club entrance where surging bodies just pushed Rob into the club. At the top of the steps, he's poking his head back out, shouting at the door guy and pointing, "Get her! I need you to get her!" There are too many people. I'm being shoved back with elbows and shoulders by fans adamant to get close, so I walk away. It's too much. I cry all the way home.

I know I missed an opportunity, maybe not the most ideal one, but I missed it and it's gone. As bad as things got with Robert, I believe he would have gone to the house with me to get my kids and help me get away from under my husband's thumb. Maybe Rob would have asked for something in return that I still couldn't give him, but I don't think he would stand for leaving me under someone else's brutal hands. I almost wish the bruise had still been there, on my face, so he could have just known without me having to say anything.

It's hard not to curl up and cry in bed next to Craig when I slip under the covers. It feels like I lost my only chance for someone to help me out of this.

CHAPTER 22

In the next weeks, I continually regret failing to reach out to Rob while he was there. It could have been its own can of worms, but this situation isn't going any better and now there are children involved. The physical aggression intensifies, and I call the cops on Craig after he beats me up with a broom. He spends time in jail, but I know he's coming back soon, and he'll be angry at me for putting him there.

Suicide starts flaunting its charms again—I know, it's not the best way out, but the possibility of not having to deal with men anymore seems like heaven. No falling in the trap again, ever. But my eyes always land on my kids and I pick them up and snuggle them on the couch. I try to be the best mom I can be, but I know the only reason I'm still here is them. Abandoning them is unthinkable, same with leaving them to any potential neglect or abuse.

The biggest thing is… I don't understand. Craig loved me so much. I know I broke his heart when I was in love with another person, but it was years ago. And no one was in the wrong, it's just what happened. Things he criticized Rob for in the past are now part of Craig and I's usual interactions. Almost like he's trying to get back at me. Even more like my old relationship, Craig wants me to stay with him no matter what. Even when it's not working, just plain awful, or I'm sobbing in pain. Even when he's angry, frustrated, or belittling me, he still wants it to be me. No one else.

He previously disconnected the house phone so I couldn't have outside communication, so it's a shock when my sister arrives at the door. My first impression opening the screen is her round, eight-months-pregnant belly. As my eyes drift up, her concerned face makes it too hard to even try to pretend I'm okay.

She's been worried, says she had a dream about me where I was dying and for some reason the dream ate at her and she couldn't let it go. When Craig ambles over, putting a hand on my shoulder, and asks why she's here, my sister doesn't take jack shit from him.

"I know you hit her. She's my sister, and we're going. She's leaving now."

I thought he was going to hit her, pregnant and all. As I tuck the twins into her car, she stands at the door front, blocking him from leaving.

"You're staying here," she says to Craig. "You can keep playing house by yourself, but you're not going to kill my sister." I leave with almost nothing. I take my babies, the car seats, and a few changes of clothes in a small bag, and we escape to New York. My relief doesn't last long. Craig serves me papers across state lines, saying I abandoned the property in Florida, which is illegal in the state. The judge who orders me back to resolve it, sets in place his own functional boundaries so we'll work it out. Meaning the judge puts Craig on the first floor and me on the second until everything is in order. I spend each evening hoping it's not the night I'm beaten so badly I never make it out again.

I'm responsible for the mortgage because my name is on the loan. Even though he's wealthy and has his own place from his parents, he's forcing pressure on this. All to make a point. I've had enough and I want out. I sell the house. Naturally, he takes most of it and gives me a little in between a back-and-forth court hell drama that also involves the custody of our kids.

I try not to think of it as a scorecard, but it feels like I've let two partners down. I couldn't be enough, or I didn't do it right, so they tried to fix me and failed.

Impressions of moments are hard to change. Sometimes the reminiscence becomes better and clearer than the moment itself. I still remember my hairstyle the night Robert pulled me out to the fire escape to talk about my pregnancy and how he didn't want a child. I remember what I was wearing, what he was wearing… I remember the sky and the way the light from inside hit his face. It almost turns it into a fond memory, like my emotions are trying to deceive my mind. My memories with Craig are like that too.

I move on again. I have to. I spend years working on myself, a career, good lives for my kids. Nothing in me wants to mess that up again, but—naturally—humans are prone to error and no good deed goes unpunished.

PART 2

CHAPTER 23

"I'm a victim of R. Kelly. I met him in Florida as an underage kid."

This is the statement that started an avalanche of changes in my life. I emailed Buzzfeed, requesting to speak with Jim DeRogatis months after reading his BuzzFeed article outing the R. Kelly harem. The cult.

Prior to this, I tucked everything as far away in my mind as possible and did everything I could to not raise the memories. I had planned on letting everything rest forever. Run away from the past, swallow it down and let it rot inside of me alone. I could handle it. Then I saw parents, mothers, aunts, and sisters… all trying to protect their children and nieces, seeking justice, and I knew everything was about to be different. That single sentence roused Jim's attention. He emailed me back directly, starting a back-and-forth conversation that very night.

Little did I know, Jim had been hunting me down for years. Over twenty, to be more precise. He knew about me, had been following the trajectories of Rob's relationships for ages, but couldn't look me up because he didn't know my last name. I was simply *The Spanish Singer Girl from Miami* for the longest time.

"I've been waiting for you," he said.

"Really?"

"You're the girl from Miami. Aaliyah's uncle mentioned you, Barry Hankerson, he told me about you when the first trial was about to happen. He said to me, 'Find that girl. If anyone can put him away, he did a number on her.'"

***

R. Kelly abuse allegations explode into my life in the summer of 2017 for the first time since he was acquitted in 2008. It all starts with BuzzFeed's July 2017 article: "Inside the Pied Piper of R&B's 'Cult,'" written by a man named Jim DeRogatis. Three women out R. Kelly in print for his supposed "guest house" where he keeps multiple females under complete control through coercion, abuse, and strict rules denying them access to friends and family. My stomach sinks deeper as I read further, by the end of the article, I'm on the floor, shaking. It's too familiar. Not entirely surprising, but that's still some messed up shit.

Another woman, Jerhonda Pace, who met him at age sixteen at his trial for child pornography, adds her harrowing account in August, mentioning an unidentified friend she hopes will step forward eventually as well. It feels like women are popping out of the woodwork all over, and all with horror stories about Rob running every aspect of their lives.

For years I've focused solely on letting the dirt with Rob slide off my back, distancing it as much as I can so it can scar over and heal into some form of acceptance. But this is a pattern, and patterns continue if they aren't stopped cold. Hearing R. Kelly is hurting women ain't nothing new, and I've tried to shut it out every time. But the voices of the parents, their pleas, the words of each woman's detailed account... I can't shut those out. God knows I try. Knowing that hiding my pain allowed this to continue happening to other young women, eats at me. I did it for self-preservation, but in the end, it meant other girls had to experience the same level of stuff that wrecked me.

Reaching out sounds terrifying, and I start multiple introduction emails to Jim that I delete with shaking hands. This cannot in any way be about ruining the man I once loved and gave everything to. How do you come out about someone you loved? Not just in a private police case, but to the world, because of his fame. It's not fair for any heart to ever have to do this. It feels like betrayal. I read and reread the articles, my stomach knotting tighter and tighter. It was so long ago, what help am I now? *You know, Lizzette, stop kidding yourself.* I'm another voice, another pillar of support, another victim to stand with the others and validate their pain and everything they've lost.

Everyone involved in this circle of abuse should know they are not alone, see other survivors, and not feel silly for caving to Robert for so long. He's compelling, he's got the cycle down pat, and it's not wrong to open up and trust people. We need to stop beating ourselves up for trusting someone who hurt us. No, I can't let this go. Even if I tried, it's hovering now, always, in the back of my mind, eating at me.

It isn't until March of 2018 that I give in. Life is busy and I'm working for Benihana as the project coordinator on a construction site, dealing with new business renovations. I have a beautiful apartment that overlooks the coast, both beach and ocean, in Aventura, Florida. The same place I met Rob. Ha, the irony. I go to work in a convertible Fiat, my kids are in private school, and I'm in a healthy relationship with a new boyfriend. We've been together four years already and continue to get along well. After all the shame and destruction that came from living for other people, it finally feels as though I'm living my best life for me.

Despite my reservations, the moment comes when I press send on the message to DeRogatis. Then I crack open a bottle of wine, trying not to full-out panic.

Things don't go smoothly just because I reach out. Establishing that connection is not a moment of relief, as if the words are now out in the universe and I can go to bed and sleep soundly. Jim is working on a story about Dominique Gardner and her mom, and he wants to include my story with hers, or at least around the same time, for solidarity... and greater effect. Meaning he wants my story out and ready. Now. It's hard to rush re-experiencing and reliving trauma to a stranger. At the same time, they were all hurt by the same man, and they were strong enough. Freaking heroes, to be honest. We need each other. All of us were by ourselves trying to figure it out alone for too long.

Work on the article starts with a bunch of questions, including, can he talk to Michella, *AND* can he speak with my mom. Michella? Easy. Done. My mother? Ehhhh...

"Leave it alone, Lizzette! It's not important anymore."

"Mom. I'm letting you know they're calling whether you say yes or not. I never ask you to do anything for me. Can you please just do this? It doesn't have to be long. He wants to confirm a few details."

Pleading and coaxing go on for a while, and eventually she succumbs to at least answering the phone. On the other hand, there's no guarantees on what she'll say.

By the time the request for photos comes in, it's May, and my small family has already resettled in an adorable cottage smack dab in the middle of Little Havana. A photographer for BuzzFeed is sent to my home to take my portrait and hopefully figure out logistics and such, but next thing I know, the story goes to press a couple days after the photoshoot. It's a surprise to me—never had the opportunity to review what

Jim and the photographer put together between interviews and the photography session—but I know they want to get it out quickly. Otherwise, the media wave started by the other women loses speed. Jim sends me the article immediately after it hits the internet.

My fingers tremble as I scroll down. The title of the piece is, "He's a Predator," with a giant photo of me at the top. Not just any photo, it wide pans to show my entire front porch. My fingers keep scrolling as the screen reveals more photos. Each picture making it more and more obvious where I am, on A Street, like a bright red target. These are photos of where I live… currently, right there on display for the internet to see. My new place. My recently acquired home that's in the middle of a pedestrian, tourist zone. My home that I'm sitting in at this moment. I thought we were taking pictures outside for *the light*. These aren't portraits, I'm not even the focus in all of them.

Keep scrolling. *My job. No.* My workplace is listed there in black and white. Where I physically show up to work every day. Blood rushes out of my head and dizziness hits. I want to throw up. I rest my head on the table, trembling. Even my legs are shaking. We're on a main avenue for foot traffic. Anyone who reads this article will be able to pick out which house I'm in, especially since it lists the neighborhood directly underneath—in case anyone wasn't from Florida and didn't already know how easy it would be to find us…

My parents call me up to let me know the photos don't really look like me, and to ask why my house is in the pictures. No good response to that.

I wanted my story out there. I wanted my story out there. I keep repeating it to myself as I leave my coffee untouched on the counter and sink onto the floor of the shower. Tears already streaming down my face, I lean against the shower tile and let the water run over me as rage starts to consume the fear. Fear has held me back for so long because of Rob's extensive, influential reach, and now everyone knows where

I work and live. All of Florida, the rest of the U.S., even foreigners. All that extra information. Why did I think I could handle this?

Next thing I know, BuzzFeed is contacting me again to discuss a documentary that's already in the works, and paperwork is showing up for my review. At least there's legit paperwork this time. My unease about revealing my past to the public tripled with that last surprise. I spoke up to *not* have to live in fear anymore, and now I absolutely live in fear of my compromised safety. At the same time, standing with the other survivors seems bigger, more important. A documentary could have a real impact. And if they're putting our faces and personalities on the screen, they must have some kind of plan in place to assure our safety. This isn't a production that would release without lasting repercussions.

I take my time reading through every slip of paper. No requests or demands for videos of my home. *Just checking.* Despite the voice in the back of my head saying it's too much, it'll affect the rest of my life and there's no reverse button, I remind myself of all the women it's going to help. It's not just me. That's the whole point. I can't think only about me.

But also, once I get this out there, off my chest and into the ears of other survivors or potential victims, then I can let go, and we can let go, and the world will be infinitely brighter for the women who won't experience the same pain I did. I keep reminding myself: BuzzFeed wants to help. They're requesting a signature right off the bat, no waiting. My jaw clenches with worry as I put my pen to paper, but I sign. I've missed too many opportunities by not directing the course of my own life.

Right after the article releases, we start having attempted break-ins in Little Havana and I'm afraid to both leave the house and stay in it. Watching the front door jiggle becomes a night watch sort of duty. My twins are traumatized, wanting to sleep anywhere but here.

Everything is happening so fast, and everyone says they want to hear my story, to make sure I'm heard by the world. When I sign for the BuzzFeed documentary, I'm told someone named Lyric Cabral will be in charge of the project and working with the survivors. I get a message from her about archive needs and she says she'll be in touch.

Finally, a contact point I can talk to consistently. Curiosity plunges me quickly into the depths of the internet where I discover she's an Emmy-award-winning documentarian, notable for a film called *Cara*. Hooray, someone legit who knows what they're doing.

When Lyric reaches out, she requests all kinds of random physical evidence of my former life to add to the "archive" she's setting up. She wants pictures, music I've written, hospital records, anything that will offer credibility or depth to the story of my life. My response probably isn't what she wants to hear.

"Okay. My mom has most of that stuff, but I'll warn you, she ain't giving up shit because she's a narcissist." Silence on the other end. "I'll work on it?"

The days go by and the network keeps dragging their feet, leaving me wondering if this is ever gonna happen. The film is supposed to be produced by Buzzfeed in a partnership with Hulu, meaning it's going big, until one substantial problem comes up—Hulu forms a marketing pact with Madison Square Gardens. They're now partners, and R. Kelly has a show coming up at that very venue. Hulu opts to let the concert happen, in conflict with the documentary they just promised to release that outs their headliner. Surprise, surprise. Buzzfeed shows a soul and pulls out, citing a conflict of interest on Hulu's part. Aaaaand we're back to square one of this bullshit. I'm still looking out my windows at night, checking for angry R. Kelly fans, and the effort we've put in so far is meaningless.

Enter Lifetime. Stage right.

CHAPTER 24

I'm reviewing details on upcoming Benihana projects when Lifetime contacts me midsummer about another documentary proposal, turning my life into a whirlwind of "everything is going to happen *now*." A woman by the name of Tamra Simmons, working with Kreativ Inc., is an executive producer taking a docuseries idea to Lifetime to reveal the stories of women abused by R. Kelly. A similar project to the Buzzfeed undertaking but on a larger, more widespread scale.

The parents of a young woman named Joycelyn, still under Robert's thumb, had passed along my number to Tamra after contacting me weeks before. They had been searching out the other women who had come out publicly about Rob. Sort of a who's who deal—make sure I'm a real person... I am. Not just lying to be part of the publicity... I'm not. This isn't fame, I almost want to warn them, this is practically infamy. It's putting a target on your back. R. Kelly fans are dedicated to the bone, and anything that's been pushed off and swept under the rug for this long is not going to be shaken out easy. No one wants hatred and death threats, but for me, it's already on my doorstep and I can't go back.

Joycelyn's parents are going to be in the documentary, and I understand why. It's their way of trying to reach her. They're down to last resorts just to find her. Tamra tells me she's delighted to chat with me and emphasizes the fact that I was underage when my relationship with Rob started. I think the audience shock factor is just as important to her as the illegality. She seems to believe it's essential to include me, so I cave. Underage women were and are being groomed and exploited for his benefit. Caving seems like a good thing. I'm ok with caving today.

Full paperwork arrives with a noted caveat: all the company has is $1,000 left in the budget to pay me. I'm not really sure how this aspect is normally approached or what I should be expecting financially to discuss my rape and abuse on film. It seems almost unethical to ask. I was thinking less about a chunk sum and more along the lines of them taking care of expenses like travel, appropriate clothing, hotel stays, and contributing to counseling, mental health care, and personal safety during all this. Hadn't really thought hard about a proper paycheck before. A thousand dollars is significant, right? Honestly, I have no idea. Whatever. I'm helping other women and that's really the key here. It's basically the same as volunteering to speak to survivors at an assembly, right? Just on a grander scale? From what I've heard, this whole project is for the greater good.

Not wanting to miss anything this essential for change, I shrug and sign. A thousand will have to do. It's more than not having it, and I assume it means the producers are working on a minimal budget.

Amid all the documents, various contacts, emails, and whatever other madness takes place as everyone attempts to coordinate and contact each other, the word "lawyer" never comes up. Much less, hey, maybe get a lawyer *to make sure all the details are taken care of for you* or *so there are no surprises*. Or, you know, just because it's a good idea in general when your face goes on screen for something controversial. Cheers, we care about your well-being, get someone to help you out already because we won't have the time or resources. That last one would have been extra nice.

Before I know it, I'm being flown out to L.A. and settled into a hotel room amid a flurry of activity. It feels like I've hardly dropped my suitcase in my designated room, and I'm being called to show for hair and makeup. Anxiety meds, don't fail me now.

By the time I reach set, I can hardly walk straight my legs are shaking so bad. This production team is trying to get stuff done quick, and you can feel it in the air. The atmosphere is hurried—fast movement, quick changes, get in and out, get here now, fingers snapping for the assistant's attention, and so on. I can feel the pressure and tension rolling off everyone I meet. If my nerves completely fray and explode to pieces right now, at least I'll know I went with good intentions.

Since I'm not really savvy on how to dress to talk about my abusive relationship (who is?), I'm in a safe pair of jeans with a black top. Seated in a back dressing area, waiting, everything about my former relationship starts leaking into my stream of thoughts—our first seat at the piano in the studio, jumping the gate in heels with Michella, my shame in the bell tower, Rob's absence at the ICU… three times… it's a flood I can't turn off. Thankfully, the entrance of a kind-faced woman tears me away slightly, giving my nerves a little relief.

"Hi, Lizzette. I'm Dream Hampton, it's nice to meet you." She reaches out a hand, which I shake. "I'm here to work with you on styling for your interview." As Dream chats and bustles around a bit, my shoulders start to loosen. I didn't realize I was clenching them so hard, trying to pull back into an imaginary shell. My brief hiatus from the avalanche of memories, though, helps me smile back and loosen slightly. It doesn't last long.

"I thought you said you had *pictures* of you and Robert!" Tamra Simmons, executive producer, barges into the space shouting and glares at me as though I tricked her.

"Um, I never said that 'cause, you know, Robert kept me a secret. Why would he let me take pictures? He was married most of the time." The rage eye contact hasn't stopped yet so I keep going, "Like, he would make me put my head down in cars so no one *could* take a photo. He didn't want evidence, but at the time I thought it was a privacy thing…"

Now the emotions are starting to bubble up again as my anxiety seizes control and starts smearing more coherent thoughts into a blur of fear and panic. Please, you're not even on the chair yet, don't have a panic attack now. Clutching my chair, I distantly hear Dream telling Tamra to calm down. "Don't get into her like that. It's not her fault. Come on, give us some space… Tamra, don't treat her like this. That's not why she's here."

Tamra, however, is still here, eyes wide. Regaining hold of myself, I eye her right back. *Bitch, if I had a picture of him and I, you would have to pay me so much fucking money just for a glimpse of it.* Meanwhile Dream apologizes and ushers me off to the interview itself. Excellent timing, now that my resolve is cracked and my nerves are on the verge of shattering into confetti.

Occupying the interview chair is like climbing a mountain. I can't get enough breath, my heart is pounding, and it's exhausting. I break down a lot. Tearing up and walking away from the chair is a continual yet steady pattern for keeping it together. My entire being is in flight mode and ready to bolt, so some kind of adrenaline-based "survival" Lizzette takes over and keeps spitting out words even when internal me can't handle it. Then my brain starts shutting down before we're even halfway through, which is when my memory starts skipping, and by the end, it's all a blur.

My little scrap of self-protection awareness bit down so hard to protect me from my own story, I can barely remember the specific words used, just the hangover feeling it all leaves behind. Bits and pieces break through, as though poking the trauma again made it rise up and try to erase itself unsuccessfully. My mind built a shield to protect me, but it's making me feel stuck in darkness instead.

As I try to push myself out of my seat at the end, my swollen eyes can hardly stay open and I'm not sure my legs will hold me. Everyone has basically scattered for a coffee break. The reignited grief in my gut is burning a hole that makes it hard to stand up, but there's no social worker in sight, no counselor. Nobody pays attention to me now that I'm out of the hotseat.

All those hours in a chair for that long, reliving things I haven't spoken about in over twenty years—things that changed the course of my entire life—and there's no one to address trauma? No counselor? I would happily take a therapy dog. Therapy mini horse? Herbal tea.

Wobbly and disoriented, I totter back to where I left my things. I hear Dream's voice behind me, "You know... I know a lawyer." Hanging my head so I don't have to make eye contact, I continue shuffling through my purse. When will all this embarrassing shit stop already? She keeps talking, "That part about the STD, that's not okay. You should have had a lawyer for that kind of stuff."

I appreciate the kind intentions, the caring, but there are *so many things I should have had a lawyer for with Rob.* How does a lawyer cover all of them now, this late? Not to mention, I don't want to relive this outpouring of trauma again, not in a courtroom full of people. Tell the world I got an STD from R. Kelly? That he stole my virginity before I turned eighteen? Explain the many, many times I felt I didn't have any control over my own life? I already lived and relived that nightmare. I don't want it to have another life, that's why I'm here. Get it out and done.

"Yeah," my mouth attempts a smile, but I know it looks fake. Strained. "I'm probably not going to pursue that specifically with Robert right now. Going public from behind the lens is pushing my limits." Goddamn these tears coming back up again. "I already have to live with the STD and the fact that it comes out when I'm stressed and all."

Dream offers me an empathetic smile and glances down at her schedule before she turns and walks out, stopping a couple feet outside the door. She's clearly stopping a passing assistant when I hear her ask, "Oh, is Demetrius here?"

My heart drops. *No, no, no, no, no. They wouldn't.* They wouldn't do this to us. To me. Not directly after I had to go through all that. No, these mothafuckers do not have Demetrius Smith, R. Kelly's main man who was there for all of it, everything I went through, here in this building at the same time. Tremors rock my hands. Why is this happening? Just to remind me what it's like to feel like a stupid little girl again? Gasping for a full breath, I slip out the side of the stylist tent and scurry to an area out of the main premises, far enough I probably can't run into anyone.

Ten or so cigarettes later, I'm together enough to force myself back in the mix to find a ride back to the hotel. Once inside my room, I can't hold back the sobs anymore. It feels like everything is caving in. My head and limbs prickle with anxiety, an electricity that at least reminds me I'm still alive. With time, my body wears itself out and I drift into a dull buzz reminiscent of a hangover. My soul feels scraped out and my head aches.

Black clouds settle over me and I consider never leaving the room again, just letting it end here. Picking up the phone and explaining the pain sounds like energy I don't have. Besides, there's no one. No one here to talk to, no one to call. My therapists are far away and no one from set offered numbers for "just in case" after reliving all that pain.

Locking my door, I fall into an uneasy sleep, knowing Demetrius is close by, telling his portion of the same stories. No one thought to tell me in advance or split our days up? Does Tamra not get it? Our production team doesn't seem to understand PTSD. My mind keeps racing as I dip in and out of sleep. The next day, I get up early and fly back to Florida with relief.

***

It doesn't take a rocket scientist to realize opening up that rabbit hole of torment wasn't worth one grand, but get this, I don't even get a thousand dollars. When I arrive back home, I receive a check for five hundred, followed by a phone call saying I need to come back to reshoot the interview with a different host. The other half of the payment will arrive only on completion of the documentary (providing that happens), and the thousand doesn't account for taxes. Huh.

Already on the verge of a breakdown, I'm trying to pull it together. Since returning to Miami, I haven't heard from anyone involved in the docuseries other than the alert about repeating the interview process. Not so much as a "thank you" or "how are you holding up?" Questions about having to repeat the process are generally brushed aside and my flight out is scheduled for a second time. This one in August.

While I was away, disturbances on our property increased. The harassment has everyone on edge. That initial bout of negative attention directly after the article had already left us wary and stressed.

Enough is enough.

My hands are slick as I pick up my phone to dial my rep. The unreality of it all vibrates in the back of my head like a drone, evolving into what's about to be a killer headache. By the time someone answers, my hands are shaking so hard I have to set the phone down on the counter and tap a few times to hit the spot that engages speaker mode.

"Hey, those photos on that Buzzfeed article, they show my house. Everyone knows where I live. We need them taken down; we don't feel safe." I'm breathing hard, leaning against the counter with my head in my hands. She attempts to calm me with reassurance that she'll talk to Jim DeRogatis.

Buzzfeed confirms they'll try to pull some of the photos down. The obvious ones at least. Not the most comforting news, but there's not much else I can do. It's recommended I keep checking the site for updates. With a mumble of resignation—and *possibly* a curse under my breath—I leave DeRogatis alone to wait for the updated site. The next several hours are spent reloading browsers with a glass of wine in hand and panic-calling close friends.

True to their word, they pull photos, but not enough. Besides, at this point, so many people have already seen them. The cottage is distinct enough to pick out from the street without much effort. This place is marked.

As the days slink by, it feels like Pandora's Box opens in my chest. All the emotions, the hurt, the memories, those tiny splinters of awful moments you've almost forgotten about that live under your skin … all come crashing over me. I've put so much effort into sugarcoating different scenarios and decisions so I could live with them. Even during filming, I didn't realize quite how much I was still hurting.

The ache that comes with these memories turns into a cloud of dark despair. I can hardly interact with people, much less leave the house. The phone call from Lifetime telling me I need to come back and do everything from scratch sounds like torture.

My retake with Lifetime arrives, and I'm told to bring two outfits this time—one white and one black. Between recently moving, purging for a smaller living space, and all the madness lately, I don't have exactly what I need on the spot, but it'll work. I have an alternate outfit packed as well, just in case. The white getup is easy. I have a pretty, white skirt and matching top, just a little too fancy for work but still professional in appearance. I don't own the right kind of all-black outfit, but I can mix and match, so it's still black and white, or wear black pants. Into my suitcase, I tuck a long, soft black shirt, almost long enough to be a dress, followed by a white skirt. To, you know, make sure the extras are definitely covered.

For the second time this year, I find myself stepping out of a tent after perfecting my makeup to relive heartache and some of the most difficult parts of my life in front of strangers with a camera crew. I take a slow, deep breath before hustling towards set, but I'm stopped long before I can reach the interview chair.

"No." Someone with a badge on a lanyard is flurrying a hand at me as they look me up and down and continue talking on their cell.

"No?" I peer down at my shoes. "Sorry, you're going have to be more specific ab—"

"Whatever that is, take it off. You don't need it." They gesture at my skirt.

"Oh, it's really short without it, it's not meant to be a dress. It's a shirt."

"Only the dress on, okay?"

"But it's a shirt."

"The top is fine. No white skirt. Don't worry, we're only shooting you from the waist up."

"Then why does it matt—"

"We'll see you back here in five."

Retreating to the tent to change, I slide the white skirt over my knees and past my ankles, step out of it, and look in the mirror. Oh god. I don't think I'd let my teenage daughter wear this in public. They aren't really going to let me go out like this, right? Pretty sure after one look at me, they'll turn me around again to put something back on. Is it messing up their lighting or something to have the white bottoms?

After a few pained moments of uneasy twirling in front of the mirror to see the different angles, I scootch out the door and take little steps, holding my "dress that most definitely isn't a dress" down with pinched fingers the whole way.

When I finally reach the lanyard-wearer again, I edge my way up to them. "You know, it doesn't really cover…"

Flashing a glance at me, they interrupt, "It's fine. Like I said, we're shooting from the waist up. Don't worry. It's really just the black top we need."

"So then can I just…"

"Sit, please." They're adjusting my hair as I try to squeeze the ends of the shirt as far down my thighs as possible. "And, she's ready!"

Well… now I feel anything but ready.

"I'm really uncomfortable without anything under this shirt, can we please change it?"

Our interviewer studies me briefly, "It's fine. Like they said, it won't matter. Camera cuts won't dip below the waist. We're essentially shooting in portrait mode, close up."

Crew members scuttle around me, making sure mics are right, anyone with a speaking part has water, and everything is perfect. Minus the minor detail that I'm not wearing pants. Every time I open my mouth to ask again, everyone looks elsewhere or doesn't respond, busying themselves with some small task. I stop trying and focus on getting through the day. Reliving Trauma: Part II. This round includes the added effort of squeezing my crossed legs together as hard as possible while responding to intensely personal questions.

Coming back to Florida sunshine sounds warm and breezy, the perfect balm for reopened emotional wounds, but my stability is melting from underneath me. Somehow, lots of people seem to know about my involvement in the docuseries, which is unnerving. Then, after sitting through a deposition in addition to the recent filming, any part of my long-constructed preservation shell that hadn't been cracked or worn away already is pulverized to dust. I didn't know it was possible to feel more extremely than I already have, but the emotions and memories slam down on me, cracking through level after level of pain. This is when I start the process of losing everything.

CHAPTER 25

It's hard to face truth when you've spent years sugarcoating reality to keep getting through your day. At this point, I've painted so many layers over the past. Pry them back now? Hell no. Except I already started the process and now these raw memories are bulging at the seams, threatening to tear apart the life I've built. Between my already deep-seated depression and newly awakened severe anxiety, I can hardly show up to work much less do anything substantial.

Not long after the second filming, I undergo a surgery which requires heavy doses of medication on top of what I'm already taking for depression and anxiety. When I start feeling too sick and overwhelmed to function in daily life, I have to go see my doctor again to balance everything out. Noting that I'm physically ill at this point from both surgery recovery, prescription combinations, and the stress of reigniting old wounds, my doctor at the Segal Institute puts me on short-term disability with medical leave. From here, I go on more intense meds with a close watch on medication management to turn the episode around.

Not enough money is coming in on disability to keep our own place, so we break our lease and move out of our sweet, little cottage. We're packing everything we can and setting it up in my dad's place: me, two nineteen-year-olds and two dogs. Since it's a huge downsize, we're forced to give away a lot, and it means I'm living in the garage. At least my kids are with me and not being threatened. On the downside, one of our pups is taking the move rough, putting him on edge. His difficulty adjusting means lots of accidents, so I'm constantly cleaning up after him in what little space there is.

And just like that, the life I spent years reconstructing crumbles to pieces. Can't work, can't afford my own place, can hardly face each day without extreme anxiety waltzing in and sending me into a panic attack or totally shutting me down. Beautiful office and condo have turned into living off disability in a garage in the course of months.

Almost as though the universe knows I can only handle so much, the fates coincide for a job offer in El Segundo, California. My father encourages me to take it, assuring me he can be there for the twins if they need anything. I move from Miami to California in September 2018, ready to start making eighty grand a year and get my life back. Insomnia and such are still going strong, but it's been too long already and I feel that it's time to try again. Work will be good for me. I hope.

I go for it, following the work out to California, as well as an L.A. guy named Peter, who I met while living in my dad's garage. No, he was not living there too. Naturally, I'm wary—I know my current emotional state isn't the hardiest right now—but we have to break beyond our past at some point and at least try to live, right?

Peter and I met a little before the job offer. He's an actor by profession, so he understands the messy mechanics, sharp ups and downs, and woes of the entertainment industry. The uprooting seems like a positive on both the work and relational side. I'll have a steady job again, a regular income, and much-needed support from another adult who gets it. My kids are staying in Florida for college, so they plan to continue holing up with my dad for now. I'm not sure what else I can do for them at the moment. Reflecting on the fact that I'm about to make eight grand a month is like taking a warm bath. It soothes my soul just enough to reassure me that life will work itself out.

Once *in* California and about to start the new position, I have immediate reservations about my whole plan. Maybe it *is* too soon. Peter insists it's a bad idea, not ideal for easing back into the workplace. I would be running projects between California and Mexico as a procurement manager for resorts, overseeing renovations and traveling frequently. It's a great job, and I'm dirt broke, still half expecting to wake up in a damp garage each morning, so there's that.

While wrestling with my decision to start working, Lyric Cabral from the BuzzFeed documentary requests a meetup almost directly upon my arrival in the Golden State. We talk about where the project is at currently after the setbacks, and I explain that I'm on the verge of starting a new position. To my surprise, she's miffed. She wanted to meet up because Buzzfeed found backing again, so the documentary is going to happen after all. We're close to go time—again.

"But we're going to start soon," Lyric rests an elbow on the table to lean in towards me, "I'm taking you to Miami anytime now to film. Also, we're going to have you speak at the Hosanna 4 Youth event, it's a group focused on helping sexual and physical abuse survivors, mainly kids." Her energy and excitement, though deep-rooted, are sparking and fierce. Almost contagious… I cock my head and fold my hands in my lap.

"…Okay, but this has been pushed off so many times. I came out here for this job because I don't have money right now. I've lost basically everything, and I need this for my kids."

She shakes a hand at me. "I'll write you a check right this minute to get it started. And so you have some money to get by, but *don't take the job*. We're going to be filming soon, and you already signed a contract with us."

Unknown to me until this moment, BuzzFeed has finally released the money to start filming, which means Lyric writes me a check for $7,500. As much as I'd like to pour it into a relaxing spa trip to the Bahamas (which, let's be honest, I could absolutely use at this point), I set aside most of it to rent a tiny apartment for my kids so they can move out of their grandpa's house.

Even with the check, a large part of me is still clutching to the security of a full-time, well-paying job. I might have tried to juggle both if it wasn't for the debilitating insomnia, plus the fear of breaking contract terms with a large company like Buzzfeed. Anxiety is a never-ending plague. When do I finally find rest and recovery? Are normal emotions too much to ask for right now?

Maybe Peter is right and trying to power through a new career opportunity in this state of mind will end up in disaster. I just picked up my entire life and flung it across the country, so I'd better be on board with the few people backing me.

It's decided. Instead of going back to Florida, I'm staying in Los Angeles on medical leave at Peter's place. Relaxation and time to heal can only help at this point. My brain lately feels like it's falling apart and floating into a million pieces far away from me. Some grounding sounds ideal. The company warns me they can't wait for me, which means I'll be applying for more permanent disability until the $30,000 comes through when BuzzFeed filming is complete.

I apply for long-term disability after chatting with my doctor, but I'm informed there's going to be a wait before the next check since I'm switching over from short-term to long-term. Within weeks, Lyric informs me the first shoot is cancelled. I miss out on the management position, and since BuzzFeed didn't shoot with me, the next set of funds aren't released. What's left of the $7,500 is all I have to my name until things are straightened out again.

However, that worry is increasingly pushed to the bottom of my stress list because the Lifetime docuseries, *Surviving R. Kelly,* is about to premiere.

CHAPTER 26

My nerves are riding high as can be. The *Surviving R. Kelly* premiere is being held at NeueHouse tonight in Madison Square. Pre-reception is at 6:30, screening starts at 7pm, and afterwards there's a conversation panel with five survivors plus Tarana Burke, founder of the #MeToo movement.

We ladies expected the photographers and media, so all of us came out looking good as hell, despite the early-December New York bite in the air. Several of the participating survivors are here, including Andrea Kelly, Kitti Jones, Jerhonda Pace, Lisa Van Allen, and Asante McGee. I spent long hours getting my hair to look soft and smooth, and I'm wearing a tight black turtleneck, a long black leather skirt that shines under the camera flashes, and high heeled black boots. Tonight, I'm feeling classy as fuck and strong for sticking it all out this long. All of us have poured our sweat and tears and anxiety into this; we're equally parts terrified and excited to be here.

It's chilly outside, so outdoor press moments leave us huddling in ragged lines for photos, but my nerves are making me sweat despite the cold. By the time everyone gathers in the theater, pulses are racing. We women are about to see ourselves on screen divulging some of the hardest and most twisted things that ever happened to us. Our trembling fingers are clutching purses, armrests, and each other's hands or knees as the lights dim and intro music drifts in. This is it. Our moment of truth and redemption.

It never comes.

All R. Kelly survivors are seated in the theater's frontmost row. About fifteen anxious minutes in, security lurches into the front, bumping into knees and muttering something about moving quickly and shuffling us somewhere else. Are we supposed to bring purses and coats or leave them on our chairs? What's happening? Can't tell exactly what's going on… The officer's movements are jerky, almost panicky, their voices edged with warning.

We end up in a private booth area hidden on one side of the theater. Somewhere we won't be as "exposed" is what we're told. No one's entirely sure what this means yet. The full list of "survivors" hasn't been released to the public. One guard explains they don't want to leave the five of us out in the open at the very front together, where it'll be obvious who composes the contributing survivor troupe. *Open to what?*

Everyone in our group was already on the verge of tears and mentally prepared to be emotional wrecks for the night. Now we're scared.

Next thing we know, a number of police are hurrying around. One cop pokes his head in to check on us and communicate with security. I suppose it's meant to be reassuring, but it's not. They're discussing a bomb threat, someone else is mentioning a gun threat, but both have one thread in common—*the call came from a Chicago number.* My limbs go cold.

Everyone is upset, nervous, talking over each other. The threat of violence hangs heavy in the air. Security forces usher us through a back hallway, out the door, and towards a waiting van. We stick close together like glue, afraid of being individually picked out. My ears tune into every sound. Voices echo in the city streets and can be heard above the crowds. I hear rapidly chattering reporters and excited news crews. Something about an unidentified male caller. Anonymous gun threats. Claims of someone in the audience waiting to shoot if we showed the full documentary. Possible bomb threat but that's not corroborated by anyone else.

The whole night is canceled. Too risky to not take it seriously is what they say. Someone is talking to me, telling me the threats aren't credible, this is just a precaution, we're totally fine. Not feeling fine. Not fine at all.

As I climb into the van, I see Faith Rodgers through the van window, out on the freezing sidewalk, helping lead the "Mute R. Kelly" chant. Her passionate demeanor makes it clear she's doing what she feels she needs to right now. The energy she's putting off is so engaging, I almost don't notice the voice behind me and a little to my right.

"She needs to get in the van already."

"Girl," I say, "We're all in this shit together. Like stop, seriously."

"No, she needs to come in the van. *Now.*" This fellow survivor looks prepared to go out and drag Faith into the vehicle. What's she gonna do, carry her in?

"No," I insist, "she doesn't. You need to mind your business. If she wants to stay and do that, leave her alone."

"Well, you need to shut up, bitch."

I know we're all stressed, but... hold up!

"Excuse me?"

"You heard me."

"I know you talk that shit in the back of the bus, but I also know you not gonna come up here and say it." I start rearranging my things. Getting' ready, you know, just in case I need free hands.

There's a pause of consideration and a sigh. "Well, you heard me," her voice mumbles.

This bitch did not.

I look back. "I can go back there and we can get it on if you want to."

Like lightning, Drea is already hovering in between us, talking about our important connection and what holds us together. She's verging on a happy sermon about unity as we sneak glares at each other from under her elbows. Drea's thrown herself all into it—about loving each other and all and asking God for peace—and I want us to be able to trust and support each other, but I am *done* with this scene right now. So, I interrupt.

"Drea, please. Don't pray for me. Pray for yo'self. Just leave me alone. I don't like all the weird tacky shit going on. I'm not with it." She seems only a tiny bit surprised by the outburst. It miiiiiight be commonly known that I'm a tad vocal about my feelings. It's fair though, with all the times I've been stepped on, it's a means of self-protection. It took me years to start speaking up and I still feel trampled half the time.

This being such an emotional endeavor, some women involved developed this ego, like they're more important to the whole process than everyone else because they're more *recent* or they just know they had a *different kind of relationship*. I understand the deep hurt and the need after all this to feel distinguished from the larger group. You share a story and yet it's only *your* story. At the end of the day, we were all messed with and heartbroken after loving the same man and falling for the same shit. Shouldn't be attacking each other. It's not right.

By the time we pull up to the hotel, emotions are running high. Everyone is grumpy, I want a drink, and I'm happy to be getting out of this box on wheels all crammed together when everyone is stressed.

Inside the hotel, we're reaching the end of the lobby when this girl strolls up, shadowed by a larger man. She's holding up a non-descript bag, telling all of us that Robert and his camp are going to expose all of us, and he's got a file on every last woman involved. Her guy on the side is looking kinda antsy, clearly trying to maintain a casually intimidating look. As she parades the files in front of our faces, continuing to whisper threats I can't even hear because my head is buzzing, he pulls up his shirt to show us a freakin' gun!

What in the name of... Dear Lifetime, *where are our bodyguards*!? Someone is flashing a *gun* at me directly after a *gun threat* and their only thought was to take us in a van and drop us off *outside* the hotel? No one thought of escorts to rooms or ensuring we all made it to our rooms.

Luckily, a guy in charge of production (most definitely not security detail though) is walking through the lobby. Maybe he notices something is off, or maybe he's worried about the earlier threats, because he shouts out, "EVERYONE GO TO YOUR ROOMS! NOW!" I don't think twice; I scramble. I'm punching the button for the elevator like I'm doing emergency morse code or some shit.

Safe behind the closed doors of the elevator, I'm still panicking, but so is everyone else. And somehow, in the blur of all this madness, everyone ends up in Drea's room. Despite the bond of sharing near-death experiences, we're all amped up and fighting with each other—soap opera style. There's yelling, name calling, old issues getting dragged up and thrown around. Someone could make bank on this as a reality tv show right now. If it wasn't so terrifyingly intense and awful, it would probably be hilarious. More hilarious if it was not actually us.

Someone in the mix knows who the girl downstairs is, explaining to the rest of us that her name is Kash and she's also been with Rob. Apparently, she's sticking with him. With time, everyone begins to settle, calming down and huddling closer to talk, trying to figure out if Kash and her gun-toting sidekick have left yet. Once we're not *as* worried about getting shot in the hallway, we each head to our respective rooms. There's clearly a situation happening at some point during the night, but I'm not about to open my door after the events earlier. I'd like to make it to tomorrow.

Getting up in the morning is rough. We were, understandably, up late. I basically wake up in time to get dressed, pack, and head out. I trudge to the elevator, toting my luggage with a wide yawn and sleepy eyes. There's something hanging in the air between everyone, a sense of a trauma hangover from last night. My brain is overly alert, but emotionally and mentally drained. If I wasn't on edge before the trip, I certainly am now. Sleep deprived *and* worried about being killed in the lobby? Not a great combination. Especially after hearing what happened to Faith last night.

Miss Kash Jones, our personal blackmailer, met Faith Rodgers and her mom after the theater evacuation. She apparently claimed R. Kelly had a file on Faith capable of completely ruining her future if she went through with the docuseries or filed complaints. Naked photos, private information, texts, all kinds of things were mentioned. That night, Faith went into an epileptic fit from the stress after returning to her hotel room. People say words can't kill, but they can. She could have died underneath all that pressure.

This means now it's a bunch of angry, recently threatened women dragging bags across the lobby in the early morning hours. Still no security to be seen, despite the general gun threat followed by the very real man with a gun threatening every single one of us in person. As I approach the lobby doors, Drea stops dead in front of me.

"Whaaaa…" She's having a hard time coughing out the entire word. Puzzled, I follow her gaze through the glass to the roundabout for pick-ups outside.

I squint. "Drea, why does that limo have your name on it?" *Oh my god. They didn't.*

They one hundred percent did.

Mine pulls up next. A limousine with *Lizzette Martinez* written distinctly across the side. Holding back behind the safety of the doors, we scooch close together and peer in different directions, scoping for danger. We're acting so oddly that the people at both the front desk and outdoor valet are clearly confused. It appears as though no one informed them that a group of women staying in their hotel had their lives threatened last night. Twice. Huh. So, that's how the network feels about us. Lucky for me, my uncle stayed at the hotel, and is now holding my shoulder, reminding me to breathe. He's already heard yesterday's story.

Whaddya know, there's a limousine for each of us with our names printed on the side in large, bright letters. Zero discussion or hesitation, everyone starts hurrying to get in cars, practically running. No one likes the idea of being shot.

What a fun premiere trip.

My uncle scoots into my namesake limo to be dropped off in Times Square before I head to the airport. My flight is somewhat calming. As the plane nears the city, the anticipation of walking out in the open in a large, public airport starts grating at my nerves. In L.A., I get off the plane to… no one. No security, no one from Lifetime, no police, and no car. I would take the backseat of a police car at this point just to feel safe. It's better than risking the crowded sidewalks to hail a cab after all that.

Twenty minutes later, breathing a little easier in the backseat of a cab I'm ninety-percent sure isn't going to blackmail, threaten, or kill me, all the events from the last few days slam their way back into my consciousness. I cannot believe all that happened. That was unreal. Does anyone care if we make it through this alive? The negligence for our lives, our safety, it shocks me. Did survivors in other major cases like this live in the same fear I do?

***

The night before the premiere at NeueHouse, someone tried to break into the cottage in Miami with my children in it. It's the little place I temporarily rented for them in West Palm Beach. I go back and forth between staying in L.A. and visiting them at the Miami rental.

These guys broke the bathroom window to try and get in. My daughter was in there, and when the glass blew, she started screaming and ran to the kitchen to grab a knife. Kitchen knife in hand, she waited in the closet, shaking for the longest time. I guess they didn't think anyone would be home, because they left. Maybe they expected us all to be in New York already. Or just that we'd be asleep.

***

If Lifetime or anyone had any doubts about the women involved in the docuseries being endangered by R. Kelly or his people, they can be sure now: The FBI eventually arrested all the people involved.

CHAPTER 27

Madness and bullshit have a way of making people close. Between the chaos of the premiere and the media that comes with it, I become friends with Faith Rodgers' mother, Kelly. We have to rely on and take care of each other, because Lifetime isn't doing it for us.

A few weeks after the premiere fiasco, she calls me up to talk. New York had too much risk involved, and she thinks we should lock down lawyers now before anything else happens. The pressure is already on with the release date of the full docuseries coming up, but she's right, and it can't hurt. I immediately set up a meeting with Gloria Allred.

I've heard stories about Gloria. She's tough, one of the best, and constantly fighting for the protection of women's rights, which means she often takes difficult, controversial cases. My biggest fear is her brushing me off. I don't know why anyone would want to get into the middle of this mess, or what even a lawyer can do about it. The documentary releases to the public soon, I already feel silly for waiting this long to seek legal help, and my knees shake a little as I push the elevator button for Gloria's office.

After introducing myself to the sleek, no-nonsense receptionist, she walks me over to a spacious conference room and signals for me to take a chair. I have pretty much zero idea of what to expect. It's so spacious in here. It's like a cavern with a long table that looks like it was made for giant Thanksgiving dinners. I clack my nails on the table out of nerves for a bit, notice I'm doing it, and force my hands into my lap to appear more professional.

A moment later, one of Gloria's partners and another associate named Kirby enter the room, take their seats, lead with a short introduction, and ask me to tell them the specifics of why I'm seeking legal help. *Big breath.* The exhale turns into an extensive and convoluted account of the worst things and the okay things and everything in between. My listeners are kind, but clearly not entirely briefed in advance for such a mashup of events. Their faces reveal slight shock. Didn't know what they were getting themselves into being the ones to interview me.

They asked permission in advance to record me while Gloria remains in her office, watching the story unravel, making her decision whether to greet me and take me on, or not. Talking rapidly and constantly glancing around to see if anyone is bursting in, when she does appear, it still takes me by surprise. Not the hardcore, towering lawyer I expected from the gossip. A petite lady walks in with the most bomb-ass hair ever and a slick suit on and extends a hand. Everything about her is sharp and confident. She basically radiates intensity.

"Hi, I'm Gloria Allred. How are you?"

"Lizzette, nice to meet you." I'm intimidated as hell, despite her smaller stature. And I say this in a wholly impressed way. I would love to have that same kind of presence and effect on people. As Gloria sits down across from me, she motions for me to continue. I spew every detail I can think of. When my words run out, I'm informed that my statute of limitations is up. In Florida, it's been too many years to go back and hold Rob legally accountable. I knew this might be the case, but as much as I try to hold it back, the sobs break out and my entire hardened mask completely crumbles.

Gloria places a hand gently on the table, a demonstration of comfort from a distance. "Maybe he'll do the right thing. You never know. Not just for taking your innocence, but for the STD, the mental anguish, destroying so much of your life that you've had to rebuild over and over."

Through blubbering and eye wiping, I manage a nod of agreement, but it sounds hopeless to me. Robert couldn't even apologize when he was right in front of me watching me hurt.

"We're going to write a letter to him," she says in a confident, clipped voice. "A list of demands."

"Rob doesn't like being told to do things."

"All we can do is try."

My letter written out and finalized, I'm still reluctant to send it to Rob. I'm once again poking at elevator buttons with a racing heart, on my way to dissuade Gloria of its necessity while convincing myself as well. Her expression remains passive and thoughtful throughout my entire, lame rationalization speech that I know is coming from my usual former routine of appeasing Robert: Everything aims to avoid conflict, I assure my safety by reassuring him all is well. Sending this letter won't do that. It'll do quite the opposite by putting pressure on him.

As I continue to spill every anxious worry, Gloria puts a hand up to slow me and repeats her statement from before, "All we can do is try." There's hope in the air. Knowing someone like Gloria is fighting for me brings a sense of lightness after immobilizing fear.

Demands are sent out several weeks before the docuseries airs to the public. For the first time in our long history, I also ask Robert to help me financially. After restarting my life over and over with nothing because of the circumstances he left me in, the plague of hospital bills stemming from viruses passed from him to me, and the long-lasting damage to both my mental and physical health, I'm at a place where I can hardly function, and it's all directly related to him. I'm not looking for a check. I'm asking for help with therapy, healing, and getting my life back for good. His lawyer's prompt response takes us by surprise.

"I'm not R. Kelly's attorney. He has no civil attorney. I apologize, but I don't know what to tell you."

When I ask Gloria what that means for us, she sighs and explains it's basically up to Rob and only Rob then. He would have to dictate an agreement, which means the likelihood of settling anything with him is pretty much nil. It's fine, I tell myself, not the end of the world. Still can't stop the nagging feeling of frustration with his long-time music labels, though. Sony and Jive records knew what was going on for twenty plus years. There should be retribution for that for the victims, even if just in the form of counseling, for knowingly allowing this to continue. They knew. They set up my flights to meet him. I was in those rooms with him recording while he was *under contract*, making his music, their property.

Sitting in Gloria's office, going over it all in my head for the millionth time, she interrupts my train of thought. "Do you want to get out of the documentary?"

"What? Why would that make a difference?"

"It's another way he might bend," she says, "if you say you won't participate, but he's got to do something for you in return."

It doesn't take long at all to consider this. The whole idea feels like being silenced again, doing exactly what I did before, which landed me right here, right now. It would also make my journey so far somewhat irrelevant. Enduring the reignited trauma in an interview chair, the hatred from Rob's fans, endangering my family, leaving my brokenness in front of the world… the larger message that has been driving me forward would be lost. What if we ladies all did that? What would it say to the world? To young women? Then he would be allowed to keep being this way. The idea of this cycle continuing makes me feel physically sick.

"No. Absolutely not. That's selling out. We have to sound the alarms, so this doesn't keep happening."

Gloria nods in return. I leave with new intensity in my step. I leave with hope. People have judged me harshly, saying it was so long ago it shouldn't matter anymore. That is not the point. I kept my mouth shut for too long and other people's lives were destroyed by my own negligence and attempts at self-preservation. I've been poor, I've been rich, I've lost everything, and I've worked to get my life back. My dignity and respect for myself and my voice matter most to me at this point. The other women who have been hurt matter to me as well. I've already lost just about everything. This isn't about me now.

***

The docuseries releases tonight on Lifetime, and I'm a nervous wreck. Since the premiere was a no-go, I'm watching it for the first time with the rest of the world. Cozied up in my boyfriend's house in Hollywood, Lyric Cabral from Buzzfeed joins us for the watch party. Despite Buzzfeed never getting their shit together, she and I have stayed in contact as friends, waiting for the pieces to fall into place. Her goal is still to try and get more in-depth stories about R. Kelly victims for her own documentary projects, with the individual survivor stories as the main draw. She says she wants to show what really happened to me and how much Rob fucked me over.

Since the canceled premiere, I've been receiving endless threats and degrading messages from R. Kelly fans who don't want the docuseries to run. It doesn't help my nerves that I was up late reading some of them, trying to gauge how much danger I was in. To my surprise, the main aggressors turn out to be women—female diehard fans calling me a liar and professing their undying support and love for R. Kelly and his music. Considering the circumstances, it all hits me as super ironic. I was once an undying supporter of R. Kelly, I loved him, and I actually loved him—the person, and not just the music idol. My entire life was entwined with his, and now continues to be in a different sort of way. Being with him was far more important to me than his music or success. These fans are attacking me because they like his stage presence and feel moved by his art.

Worse yet, and more infuriating, my lighter skin brings out all the crazies. I'm accused of being a white woman going after black men, told I should leave them alone and focus on my own kind. The thing is, I'm not white. Both my parents are Puerto Rican. We're brown. It's awesome to watch the black female community come together in support, but there's no one coming for me, and it's crushing.

Sitting down on that couch to wait for all the stories to begin and see myself reliving the past is excruciating. My stomach feels lower than the floor and it's like my veins are buzzing with electricity. Pretty sure I'm on the verge of a full-on panic attack. When I appear in the first episode, I know everyone who presses "watch" is going to see me, even if they don't finish the series. My breathing shallows, and Peter's hand rubs my shoulder to calm me. But once the crying starts, I can't stop it.

I sob my eyes out, hands constantly raised to my face to hide the blubbering. It's not pretty. I can't even watch myself on the screen. I have to cover my eyes or sink my head into my knees or stare at the carpet—anything but look at the TV. Pretty soon, I can't even watch the other girls. Hearing these stories, such similar stories all crammed together... it's messing with my head. Reality seems to be shifting and I don't know how to feel other than lost.

At one point, my boyfriend nudges me and whispers, "Hey, so your friend Lyric? I don't trust her. She's watching everything you're doing, really closely. It seems off." I try not to look too directly, but he's right. It's like she's waiting for something, processing my reactions out of the corner of her eye. It's unnerving. Is she taking notes on how I'm processing this?

I can't finish the first episode, and leave the room with an uneasy feeling about Lyric's reasons for staying in touch.

CHAPTER 28

Soon after the docuseries is released for streaming, the FBI contacts me. They fly me to Syracuse, New York, to "talk." The flight lands on the East Coast the night before our meeting. I'm supposed to see them in the morning, and it's freezing in New York when I arrive. Like unbearably, how-can-you-breathe-in-this-air kind of cold. Since they reached out to me requesting *my* presence, they offer to book and pay for the hotel room, but when I arrive, no one has put a card down yet. I'm afraid to go anywhere else because, once again, I'll be supplying details about my past with R. Kelly after receiving threats, and there's no security and no one greeting me or reaching out to see if I landed or made it to the hotel.

My lobby experience turns into a three-hour wait for someone to figure out payment in advance of me receiving the room key. This waiting period is after the initial time spent getting ahold of the right person at the Bureau. Sitting in a plane to cross the entire country, a cab from the airport, and then a lobby for three hours does nothing great for my back. When I'm finally allowed access to my room, it feels so nice to slip under the covers and into unconsciousness. It ends too soon.

Wake-up time to greet the agents is earlier than my brain is ready for, so I try to shake the fatigue off and ease the aches out of my body with a hot shower before spending some time in front of the mirror. I'm working on figuring out the best clothing combo for warmth, comfort, and *take me seriously, please for the love of God.*

There's a fancy hotel directly across the street, which is where our chat is supposed to take place. To quell my absolute panic at, (a) Having to relive everything, and (b) Talking to the FBI for the first time ever, I chain smoke maybe six or seven cigarettes between my lobby and theirs. A solid fifty-foot distance at most. Upon arrival, I'm ushered to a chair in an out-of-the-way corner of the hotel café by five FBI agents and someone from Homeland Security. Which is right about the time I start wishing for more cigarettes.

All that's slightly alleviating my stress right now is that Gloria is here too. She stayed in the fancy hotel last night.

The FBI investigators ask for my story without much in the way of guidance, so I leap into everything running across my brain. When I make it to some of the sexual abuse, I break down and am offered a smoke break. Another six or so cigarettes in the bone-chilling cold later, I'm slouching back indoors and burst into tears the second I open my mouth anyway. Gloria, thankfully, stops the conversation a few times to give me moments of relief to somewhat collect myself.

Their questions and questioning methods aren't hostile— they're gentle people, really. Absolutely no one mistreats me in any way or gets aggressive, they're just very… in-depth. They want to dig down deep and know *everything.* Dealing with not just the memories of events, but also sifting through my brain for every detail is hard. Their need for specifics feels relentless. I'm thankful for the patience shown, otherwise I probably would have clammed up into PTSD mode a long time ago and not been able to force out a word. At the same time, they seem to already know most of the answers. It's like they're just looking for confirmation at this point, but to an insanely precise degree.

At no point do I start to feel safer than before. There are no guarantees thrown out there. No comforting words or "reach out to us if you need to." I'm assured they believe me "wholeheartedly," so I guess they realize I'm speaking the truth. One agent informs me they don't know what the FBI can do for me legally, if anything, since it's been so long. As much as it aches, I know it's true. They do express to Gloria at the end, apart from me, that they believe me one hundred percent. I briefly wonder if they said the same to the lawyers of the other survivors.

Questioning is followed by a request for me to be a "witness of pattern." Even though my personal experiences are out of date range for pressing charges, they can support and corroborate the stories of others. Also, they appreciate how passionate I am about my past and the other women. But this means I would actually have to physically appear in the courtroom at some point.

Everyone is staring at me as my heart races. I don't know if I can say yes. I might need six more cigarettes for this. I mean, who wouldn't? I'm scared. Afraid. If I go that route, I feel like I'll be in danger. I already feel in danger. I'm afraid to walk into the courtroom, or to even look at Robert. Just the thought breaks something in me all over again and I start to weep right in front of everyone. I'm afraid I'm gonna walk outside in ten minutes and someone's gonna shoot me. That's been a significant and real fear for a long time now. It haunts my dreams and lingers with me throughout the day.

At this point, the officers are talking through my lawyer anyway. They don't talk directly to me, which provides me with a little time to pull myself together. Gloria is a no-nonsense mediator. She doesn't play games, she knows all the rules, and performs her job magnificently. When they've semi left us alone, she turns to me.

"I don't know if you'll be a pattern witness. I don't know what they're doing right now exactly, but you're probably going to be one if you want to be. They cannot force you, Lizzette."

My relief is audible—a giant, heaving sigh. Gloria opens her mouth again; she's not finished.

"But I would like for you to speak."

CHAPTER 29

When another woman comes out of the R. Kelly woodwork, it's not unexpected whatsoever. I'm sure there's more of us out there who'll never come forward for one reason or another. To you ladies (and gentlemen—since it happens to you as well), I don't blame you. None of us do. It's fucking hard to stand under this harsh spotlight. I hope someone is standing there with you, wherever you are.

Anyway, this new girl is still in an "in-between mode." She hasn't entirely left Rob's group, but wants out, so she reaches out to people discreetly. You might say she's got one foot on each side of the fence. One of the people she ends up in contact with is a man named Angelo Clary. Now Angelo Clary has a daughter, Azriel, who still lives with Robert Kelly full time at one of those notorious "harem" houses. Angelo recommends to the fence-sitter girl that she talk to me.

When she reaches out, it's clear she hasn't cut ties with Rob yet. To top *that* off, this girl turns out to be Kash Jones, the woman who approached and threatened all of us with her gun-happy sidekick on the night of the premiere. Yeah, that one. This puts me on my toes, but Angelo insists she's solid now, not really with Rob's people anymore and wants to do what she can to support the survivors. Fine. I'll give her a chance. It's what we all need at some point. I get it. It can take a while to extract yourself all the way out of that mess. Took me far too damn long to leave Rob behind too.

We get into some heart-to-hearts over the phone. She saw the last couple years from the other side, so she tells me about some of Rob's reactions to the allegations and such. Tells me he really cared for me and often talked about me, that he couldn't believe it when I, of all people, spoke out against him. It's too hard to explain how frustrating that line of talk is to me, but I keep answering when she keeps calling to check in and talk through stuff. Her life with him seems to be getting harder all the time.

"I'm leaving him," Kash confesses to me one day. "I'm afraid. I'm afraid of him." She sounds sincere, and I believe her.

"I get that. Girl, if anyone gets that, it's the women in our group."

"I don't know how to say this, Zette, but Rob's been doing weird shit to me, like voodoo-level stuff. I dunno how much more I can take." She's tearing up over the phone, going into all their problems, questioning the level of danger in leaving immediately or waiting. Out of nowhere, she starts shifting gears, talking about Rob missin' me and how much he talks about me and his feelings of betrayal. *Excuse me?* This is not a conversation I want to have. I've been through too much to have this dumped at my feet right now.

"I suggest you leave him," I tell her. "Altogether. Leave that whole group behind and get away." I end the phone call soon after. She can talk about her shit, but she doesn't know nothing about Rob and I's past. Not her business either to drag herself into it. Also, I've got my own *current* problems I'm dealing with right now.

Every time I turn on the computer, I open myself up to the scathing remarks of internet trolls: "Why are you wearing that little nighty thing?" "Sure, I bet you're in this for the right reasons." "R. Kelly probably doesn't even know this bitch." And on and on.

Comment lines are packed full with jokes and zingers about me not wearing pants for my *Surviving R. Kelly* interview. The words circle in my head when I go to sleep and pound in the background of my thoughts any time I have to leave the house and go out in public. I'm angry at myself for not putting my foot down at the outfit change. But how could I have known? Also, why did I believe the directors? I ask myself the same questions every day, the color draining from my face whenever I open the internet to another captioned photo of someone teasing the inappropriateness of my outfit or comparing it to lingerie. Was this the directors' aim? To portray me this way? I don't want to think like this, but it certainly feels like I'm painted in a specific light. It's pretty clear the footage was not "as promised," just showing me from the waist up.

Sleep eludes me and I take to scrolling the internet at night, falling deeper and deeper into dysfunction as I read reviews and stress over them. That, combined with my insomnia, makes it hard to sleep at all, ever. I'm so continuously exhausted I can hardly process everything happening to me.

As days evolve into weeks, I notice Peter getting snappy whenever people recognize me. My notoriety seems to push him to some unforeseen edge. Maybe because he's an actor, struggling to survive in an already competitive world, and my involvement in the documentary puts me in the spotlight… not him. Let's note really quick here that my fame has done me zero favors lately aside from becoming a giant target. I would happily take the peace of not having stalkers show up at my door. He must understand that, at least.

Outings and nights together become tense. He starts making cruel, offhand comments that sting my recently exposed heart. I don't feel like a survivor, a warrior, or like I've overcome anything really. I feel like I'm still in the hole, waiting for someone to pull me out, truly care about me and not my past, and especially not the choices I made while I was a child, trying to be an adult.

***

The sky is dark and massive one night as I walk home. Walking helps my nerves, the unrest, the pain. Five minutes after clicking the door shut, loud knocks sound throughout the house. Luckily, my boyfriend is there. He opens the door.

"What can I do for you?"

"Wr-wrong house." A random man is standing there, looking like a deer caught in the headlights. His eyes flick to either side. I'm hiding in the hallway, breath trapped in my throat, hoping he doesn't have a weapon of any kind.

Odd instances like this continue to happen. Peter has to chase someone out of the backyard, random phone numbers call at all hours, along with threatening texts: "Choose a side," "Better watch your back," "Which side are you on, anyway?" I report everything to my lawyer, but there's not much we can do until there's a more significant physical threat, so I keep taking my anxiety meds and making sure I'm back in the house before dark if I don't have an escort.

***

My months on medical leave left time and space to start feeling better, more centered and capable. When I went looking for work, I found it fairly quickly at the L.A. Forever 21 offices as a project manager. This is where I happen to be now, months down the line, when I get some of the best news I've heard in a while on February 22nd, 2019.

Robert Kelly turned himself in.

"*R. Kelly turned himself in.*" I hold my phone tight to my ear as Stacy Kaiser, one of the consultants on *Surviving R. Kelly*, repeats herself. Shock takes my breath away until my chest begins to heave and I break down into tears. Coworkers leave me be in an empty meeting room while I cry hysterically, head in hand, a trembling arm barely holding up my phone to listen to the remaining important details. Although I'm relieved, it feels like it's still crushing me, like it's my fault Rob's getting hurt. Stacy attempts to talk me through it, "You're okay, Lizzette." Her voice is calming. "You're not the only one who is crying right now. I know you're feeling guilty, but you did not do this to him. He did this to himself."

I'm nodding at the phone in my hand as I weep. Hopefully she can make out that I'm agreeing with her, even though I can't form the words.

My Forever 21 manager, AJ, has been mad supportive the entire time and lets me know to reach out if I need anything. He knows what I'm going through, how much it's affected my life, assuring me he'll be standing with me regardless. For once, it feels like there's actual support behind me. My lawyer, Gloria, is fighting for me, Peter is providing a safe place to stay, other survivors are going through the same emotions across the country, and my employer continues to be understanding and in my corner about how difficult all of it is. A brief peace hovers over me as I acknowledge the support of others that's kept me afloat in the darker periods.

Despite enjoying my position at Forever 21, I'm only there a couple more months when my body seems to break down and I end up really sick. Unable to work, support myself, or continue to rely on Peter—who has his own stuff going on—I return to Miami, feeling defeated and hoping for help. My kids don't live in the cottage anymore, they've moved out to spots with college friends, which means I don't have a set place to stay. I start reaching out to friends who might let me couch surf or take over a spare room until I get my feet back under me.

No one opens their doors. Instead of helping, the docuseries has essentially blacklisted me both from jobs and from getting too involved in people's lives. No one wants the notoriety, the drama, the potential threatening of their household… and no one believes I'm not loaded with cash after being onscreen.

The truth is, I'm still broke as can be, and my life has been anything but glamorous lately.

I end up on different couches, slouching in and out of old friends' living rooms with my bags, shuffling in and out of the doctor's office, trying not to wear on any one person too much. Genuinely helpful souls turn out to be few and far between. The constant battle to find willing assistance, that won't ruin my last remaining threads of friendship, strains at me.

I take my meds, rest, and stay out of the way. I try to find work, but the ups and downs of my health make consistency nearly impossible. California was hard, but this is its own type of hell, so when Peter calls a few weeks later to coax me back to L.A., it doesn't take much to sway me.

I'll admit, returning to L.A. is not ideal. Peter is an alcoholic. Drunken nights mean him turning into the worst version of himself sometimes. My health will still be shit. But I can stay with him, get minimal help through unemployment, and try to make it through award show season sane and somewhat healthy. Not swapping houses all the time will help me rest in between.

It's weird to me, because the docuseries is being nominated for awards, and I feel like I shouldn't be sleeping on floors and begging for shelter. It's like going back in time to the years with Rob, left with nothing to start over.

CHAPTER 30

When Lifetime sends out requests for involvement in a second documentary, no one is shoving their way to get back in line for that mess. Most of the women from the first season of the docuseries are less than thrilled to be hearing from the execs at all.

The producers, probably knowing they aren't about to be welcomed back with open arms, give the second season a spin, claiming it'll be our opportunity to tell the world what's going on in our lives now. Thing is, no one really wants to share that with them. Many of us are still suffering with psychological and emotional problems from going through that first docuseries experience without sufficient mental health support.

They say they want the survivors to bring credibility to the table, to show that this project was created for the right reasons, not to make money off R. Kelly's situation. People all over have tried to discredit the survivors, saying we did this for money, and it's hurting the series itself. What am I supposed to say, though? No, the women who suffered through all this did not make money, but Lifetime did? Not by exploiting R. Kelly but exploiting the stories of broken women of color. Many of us were left with nothing after Rob. Many of us were left with nothing again after standing up for ourselves and trusting the networks to stand behind us.

Basically, it looks to me like this is their chance to use us again for whatever they've got going on. Aw, their viewer numbers are lower because people are talking smack? Not high on my list of top concerns right now.

And I'm not the only one who feels this way. Andrea Kelly, Rob's ex-wife, says she's out. She's not doing the second season. She goes on TMZ and talks about how they didn't treat us well or support us in the aftermath. Amen, sister.

When it seems unlikely anyone is going to bite after the last season's experience, the execs start getting creative. Sudi goes on a calling spree. Separately contacting all of us, she plays a game of, "so and so" is doing it, and "…aren't you all doing everything together? That's the impression I was under…" so we each start to think we're the only one not supporting the other women. Like maybe it'll guilt us into signing up ourselves under the self-deluded impression it was our own personal motivations.

Feeling trampled and wary, we ladies set up a call to discuss and make a unified decision about participating or not. Essentially, whether there will be a second season or not. Without Lifetime input. Strength in numbers, supporting each other, all of that. It's not just about the money, it's about the principle. At this point, many of us feel they've been disrespectful and hands-down negligent, so we want an opportunity to talk about it amongst ourselves.

I arrange and set up the call, so the phone numbers pop up on my screen when someone joins. And girrrrrl, some of these numbers are not part of our group. Some of these numbers have voices behind them that stay silent… thinking no one will know they're here. Yeah, one woman added Lifetime producers and Jocelyn Savage's parents, thinking it could be done on the sly. They can be quiet as mice all they want, but I know they're eavesdropping on a conversation that wasn't meant for them.

The conversation ends up nudged in a new direction, and everything we'd wanted before, stipulations about the media and the way we're treated, it all goes down the drain. So now some women are doing it and some aren't, and everyone is scattered and on their own separate page. No more united front.

Everything about convincing us to return evolves into bullshit games. I want to say no. Technically, I already said no. Every cell in my body is screaming at me to tell them to go jump in a lake. But they keep asking because they know I can't afford not to do it.

Financially, I'm not doing so good at the moment. Not working, despite job hunting like crazy, and running out of medical leave haven't left me with much.

Sudi, the showrunner, invites me to meet with her to discuss the "opportunity" to join them for the second season. We meet at a Thai place on Hollywood Boulevard. For the most part, she's sweet, but she still works for a production company. That company pays her rent and allows her to buy food, furniture, and fancy things. She's fished around, asked questions of acquaintances and friends, and she knows she has leverage. She knows I'm in a bad place. My take-it-or-leave-it tactics don't phase her for a second. So I switch to pressing for a decent paycheck. If it's going to affect more future jobs, relationships, and my sanity, I need at least this.

"How much you guys gonna pay me this time?"

"Well, Lizzette, I'm sorry to tell you, but it's going to be the same amount as before, because of *his* lawyers."

Yeah. Everyone got paid different. Surprised? Shouldn't be. Someone on that team worked all angles on our naivety. If we didn't know, they took advantage. Now they're trying to prove that no one is in it for the money by not increasing anyone's pay for the second season. Way to show the doubters, by hurting the women you're supposedly "supporting."

One other survivor was also paid a grand. It was a shock to her too to hear the extreme highs and lows. And no, it has nothing to do with how much we're in the news, or how recent, or how much dirt we're dropping or anything like that. It's purely who didn't have someone out there protecting them from the industry leeches in advance.

In the past, I asked repeatedly about getting help paying for therapy at the very least. Now I've got state insurance, so knowing these business execs, I don't want them involved in it. They might mess it up entirely. I don't know who their therapists would be anyway, probably would just use their own people and stick a tag on them that says "therapist." That's essentially what they did on set. They pay for consulting, but not to have a specialist on set with us. Everything about the way they run filming and people's lives feels like a game—waiting until you need something, then offering the bare minimum. As if the networks aren't making money off this. It feels like it's helping everyone but us.

I call Gloria Allred to tell her about my financial need this time around. Well aware of where I'm at, she lets me know she'll contact them and asks how much I would like to get paid. Honestly, I just need to be able to survive, be in a position that's not worse off than when I agreed to be involved. It's not their job to undo what Rob did to me, but I've struggled since the docuseries. Before all this, my life was together. Now I'm constantly falling prey to stress-induced sickness and can hardly pay rent or bills. Production knows full well that the first docuseries basically blacklisted me from certain resources and positions. Like I said before, people don't want the notoriety involved in publicly calling out a celebrity on this level.

The news isn't great when Gloria calls me back. "I spoke to them, and they're not budging." I'm trying not to let out the sound caught in my throat, the cry that's starting to shake my body. "Lizzette? Are you there still?" Gloria's voice drifts through the speaker as I slump against a wall and slide down to sit on the floor. "I think you should do it. Only because we want to put him away."

Of course I want to support the docuseries, because I believe in helping women and men who are abused. Everyone needs to do what's right for them as far as healing and rebuilding. For me, on the daily, I volunteer at a women's shelter and I'd love to work with women full time. So, yes, at the end of the day, I want to help other people more than anything. That was the initial goal and if that's all I'm going to have out of this, then it's something. I have five dollars to my name. A thousand dollars (not including tax deductions) to go through this much fear and frustration again feels like nothing, but it's more than I have right now. Peter hasn't been successful with jobs lately either, so we're both worried about getting turned out of his place with nowhere to go.

When you have nothing, even scraps are something. But how much nothing can you have and keep giving? Can nothing become a greater amount of nothing? I'm afraid what little is left will give at some point, and I'll end up in the negative somehow, unable to return to any sense of normal ever again.

CHAPTER 31

The film awards calendar overlaps both the media that comes after the first season of *Surviving R. Kelly*, and filming for the next one. Prepping for awards ceremonies is a strange adventure in itself. When I don't have the resources to pay for transportation or a proper outfit for media events, I'm once again left empty-handed by those in charge of the docuseries.

Luckily for me, during my days in New York in my early twenties, I met a guy named Bill Whitfield at the restaurant my older sister managed. He was in law enforcement, but also worked security for Bad Boy Records, so we knew people in common and had a lot to talk about. That first evening in New York, it ended up snowing pretty hard, and a group of us packed tight as sardines into his Landcruiser to drive to my sister's place in Chelsea, where we spent the whole night laughing. After that, Bill and I stayed friends over the years. He's helped out here and there when I'm in a bind, checking up on me with concern whenever the media gets especially harsh, but he really comes through for me during the Critic's Choice Awards.

Putting an end to my complete panic at not having the finances to get there, wear the proper attire or pay any other fees surrounding the whole process, Bill steps in. He helps me purchase an appropriate outfit, ensures I'll have transportation, and basically goes all out to make sure I feel like I can stand up in front of everyone with my head high. With my scrambled nerves and intense fears after the New York premiere and continual online threats, it turns out to be the extra boost I need to bite my lip, show up, and be there with the rest of the team.

We ladies sit right next to the *Surviving R. Kelly* execs at the Critic's Choice Awards. They don't look at us. They don't even acknowledge that we're here. It's as though we exist on a different plane when they don't immediately need something from us.

The arrival of the Emmys is a similar reminder: it's all about the numbers, the prestige. Survivors are placed at a separate table, a little ways away from producers and directors. It's a school lunchroom vibe. All of them in their own clique, pretending we're not part of it, even though they're only here because of *our* stories and our willingness to share. It's a balance, or it should be. Then they all get up and leave mid-show when we don't win. I don't. I'm excited to be here, honored to be here, and I paid too much just to get here looking nice enough to be a part of it all.

When I see the PR head handing out gift cards, I'm furious. I do media when asked, I literally pay to show up to things to help out or promote, but I'm not compensated for my time or efforts. Not even with gift cards. They can give out $200 gift cards to random people to promote themselves but can't give us rides, food, or security? When I take time off work in L.A. for them, they don't help with my transportation for the media we do. I don't get paid for interviews.

So I fight tooth and nail when the second round of media events starts up. This eventually gets me $400 for accompanying them to all the shows and interviews, just as a chunk sum to help with some of the expenses that came along with them. I ask for security. Nope.

"We don't pay for documentaries," is what they tell me.

"Oh, you doing it for free then too?" I ask. "Because it's my story. It's Jerhonda's story. It's *our* stories. Our faces are on billboards for you guys. We show up to interviews. People are watching us, and it is *our* lives they're following."

* * *

The tidal wave of abusive online nonsense simply keeps growing with time. Threats are getting more serious as trolls build off each other, creating conspiracy theories and other bullshit. Before filming starts, I reach out to Lyric, since she previously mentioned a company that could help. I tell her we're getting too many threats, too many negative comments online that always snowball into something terrifying. She says to negotiate with Lifetime to have a separate business both track and delete the offensive posts.

Different amounts would mean different extents of oversight, but even something simple would be an incredible relief to my peace of mind, and Lyric says it's surprisingly inexpensive. I mean, considering it's preventing physical endangerment, it's worth a lot to me. But when I talk to someone about doing it for the survivors who are up for season two, I'm told no. Once again, our safety and mental health doesn't appear to be worth the extra money.

By the time filming for the second season starts, any thick skin I had left has been buffered to nothing. The stress of endless online harassment has taken its toll. I hardly sleep. I help with press events in hopes of showing the producers that I'm willing to put in the effort for the series' success. Also in hopes that it will somewhat endear me to them, so they might care when there's a physical threat or if I become homeless.

When Sudi sits me down for the new season's onscreen interview, I'm having a nervous breakdown. She can tell something is up, but instead of backing off, she drives into it full force. I'm sure it'll be dramatic for viewers, but it's shattering to me.

Questions are usually fairly pointed in order to provoke intense emotions. This time, though, it's like they're trying to break me onscreen. If they don't with one subject, they press into something new until I start to crack, closer and closer to breaking altogether. Which is not really what I signed up for, or any of us, for that matter. Why is this now solely about unearthing and magnifying my pain? Putting Rob away by telling the truth about my past is different than breaching every emotional shield I've put up to protect myself from those days. It's emotional porn. I'm not supposed to be on trial here. I'm being torn down for sheer dramatics.

This might be a reality-based show, but it is not supposed to be a reality television game show that messes with my head until I break. Who is winning if the survivors are left in shambles? Why is it that there is still no one trying to help us *heal*?

At one point, near the end of the filming session, I'm asked, "If you hadn't walked into that mall, do you think your life would be different?" It's hard not to stare back. Honestly, it's hard not to punch something. It's said as though I partially brought this all on myself. Silly me, going to the mall as a child and accidentally meeting a celebrity who tells me they could help with my career. Yes, it seemed like fate, and no, somehow I don't think there is any doubt that if I had not met R. Kelly that day, I would not have spent the majority of my life dealing with R. Kelly.

I look around. Once again, no mental health specialist here. No social worker. No therapy dog. While on set, the showrunner presents herself as a therapist, but I've never seen any credentials, and her role here is not to personally heal or help us. Obviously.

Later, when I'm accused of flip-flopping in my responses, I want to pummel something. I was having a nervous breakdown in a chair for eight hours being asked triggering questions without any emotional or therapeutic support present. Pretending to be a therapist, playing mental games, scraping our souls raw, is not how I envisioned "help" or "advocacy." And they know me. They know my psyche, and I believe they knew full well how far I was being pushed.

If the first season's onscreen interview sessions were bad, the second were pure torture. The nail in the coffin of my stability. And I start to realize, that's what they do. No one is filming in this manner to help us recover from our past or give us hope. Our extreme pain is good for ratings. That no one is present to help us recover from the docuseries filming is the real crime right now. And what is done to me on set that day is criminal. I don't recover from the interview and I can't afford the level of therapy I would need to do so.

When I get back to the Burbank Holiday Inn where Lifetime booked my room, some of Rob's crew are casually standing in the lobby. My mouth drops open as I realize they put me in the same hotel as the people I'm accusing of misconduct. People I've openly stated that I believe belong in prison. As though it's perfectly normal to mix and mingle when there are lawsuits and legal charges and people spilling long-hidden truths to a public arena.

There's no one for me to go to, either. No enlisted security or counseling or any kind of provided help for those of us participating. As I hurry past, I hear grumbling and whispers followed by a distinct, "There's that bitch. Yeah, that's the girl doing the documentary." More grunts of recognition follow, accompanied by whispers of profanity, all aimed at me.

You can bet I pull out my cellphone to look like I'm already on a call with someone, anyone, and hurry into the elevator before jamming my finger as hard as I can over and over on the "Close Elevator" button. Once I'm in my room and have locked my door in every manner it can lock, I sit on the edge of the bed and wait for my pounding heart to slow down.

When Lifetime is later confronted by my rep to ask what the hell they were doing putting me in the same hotel as the people who previously endangered me, they deny it. When it comes up during an interview with SoCal news, they reach out to the network as well. Probably just for kicks, to put on the pressure, since it's a ridiculous scenario in the first place. After scrambling for five days to come up with a response, the best a Lifetime rep can do is, "No comment." Not, if something happened, our main concern was the survivors or anything like that. Just, "No comment."

The entire editing team walked off the project during the first season over disagreements with the direction of the series and the portrayal of the survivors. Statements I read all seemed to lean the same direction: they felt like the series wasn't actually catering to the victims and might possibly be doing more damage to them while focusing too much on R. Kelly. It humanizes him and his music by going into his childhood and family, while dehumanizing us with a lack of background. The producers ignored their suggestions and refused to listen to or incorporate any of their input.

No comment, indeed. These people know exactly what they're doing.

CHAPTER 32

I come up with an idea for a project that could help sexual assault survivors and offer me a position to use what I've learned to help others. I mention it to Stacy Kaiser, bigtime therapist and friend of mine who is involved with the R. Kelly docuseries as a consultant, telling her that I want to do something similar for assault survivors on a set like this. Beyond consulting, though, I want to physically be there for victims involved in film and media projects and make sure they're taken care of, that they know their rights and what to expect.

I bring my particular project idea to Sudi, tell her about these women from Florida who were all involved with a wealthy, well-known financier by the name of Jeffrey Epstein. She seems super interested, and I'm excited to hear back from the higher-ups.

Weeks later, a new project is announced about the women involved with Jeffrey Epstein. Except I'm not part of it. In the finance projections, they haven't included the role I intended to utilize to protect the women—doing for them what wasn't done for us. When I try to talk to someone about it or being involved in another way, just to have a job, they're dismissive. No one wants to talk to me about my story of the women from my home state anymore.

When the Epstein series does come out, it's approached differently, much the way our docuseries was described to me beforehand. They tell the story of who the women were before meeting Jeffrey Epstein. There's a level of comparison. They develop these very much real women in the viewer's eyes as genuine people with histories and lives before going into what happens to them and how it changes the courses of their futures. *Surviving R. Kelly* ended up being all about R. Kelly.

They have certain ways of doing things with certain people. They chose to do things differently.

The onset of the second season premiere and release comes with a tidal wave of messy events and uncomfortable changes.

Since I'm pushed out of the Epstein idea, I get a job at the Mondrian Hotel in West Hollywood. I'm hired as a housekeeping supervisor inspecting 120 rooms every shift. Lots of celebrities. Peter and I are friends at this point. He's been letting me ride until I can figure shit out. Our lives shouldn't be so overlapped anymore. It's not healthy, and I know I should be pressing for a clean break.

Meanwhile, Lyric Cabral's documentary falls through. Claiming she would tell our full stories in more detail so we seemed more like people others could relate to—with backgrounds and families and childhoods—we confided in her. Always under the impression she was an ally for abused women, I sat down with her multiple times to chat about the full reality of my life and past.

From what I understand, she lost her opportunity for a documentary altogether this time because she was a mole all along. After talking to us, she would head to Rob's camp and offer information on us for money. When BuzzFeed found out that she'd put them in a position like that, they canceled her projects. They don't want to get sued, and I don't blame them. That kind of conflict of interest would be over the top.

My never-ending worry about moles and personal safety skyrockets with this latest revelation. BuzzFeed then reaches out to request I immediately sign cancellation papers, which I don't do. I put aside my life for this and turned down full-time jobs. There has to be more out of it, this has gone on for years.

Then on top of all that drama, Kash Jones admits *she* was playing us the whole time and goes on her vlogging site to "expose" all of us or whatever. Nothing comes of it, and I'm not sure what happens, but somewhere along the line people stop trusting her. Unsurprising when you brag about lying for months.

When my daughter asks to visit, Peter responds with a non-committal, "Okay, whatever." She and I enjoy our time together seeing the L.A. sights. One day we're walking by the Chinese Theater and she looks over at me, slowing down to say, "Mom, you don't belong here anymore." I turn my head sharply. "Peter is not for you. You're wasting your time." Her eyes are soft, honest, and all I can do in return is nod.

That night, we sleep in Peter's living room, and take the first flight to Miami the next day. It's January of 2020, and I'm officially back in Miami. Starting over. Me and my daughter, we move into a little studio in north Miami. It's time to start living for me.

CHAPTER 33

As Robert's trial date approaches, Lisa Van Allen and I decide to go to Time's Up for public relations help. We're not getting any from Lifetime, and we know that so much of whether or not people accept us and how they treat us depends on the media and how we're portrayed. Image management is huge for our safety and future well-being in such a divisive situation. If we didn't know this before our involvement in *Surviving R. Kelly*, we sure do now.

Trial is set for September, so we contact Time's Up during the summer months, asking questions and explaining what we believe we would need. I've watched them help other women with publicity to ensure they're protected and not left to deal on their own. It's part of what they do. They can connect you with PR reps or defense attorneys—people that know how to smooth issues out appropriately and on a larger scale.

They send us to this PR girl who worked for Jive Records when all this shit was going on. At first, she's like, yeah, I'm gonna help you guys. All kindness and sweet-sounding. Then nothing happens, we stop hearing from her, and we get the sensation we've been slighted. Reaching out leads to nothing, so we're pretty sure she's avoiding us.

Not an ideal solution, but once we realize we're not getting a response, we go above her head and I contact Louise Godbold. Louise is a sexual assault survivor, now a well-known trauma specialist, and someone I know. She's worked closely with a bunch of high-profile trauma survivors and offers workshops to teach and empower other women how to help. I've always thought of her as a friend, so I reach out in an email, let her know the PR girl they connected us to has disappeared.

I'm worried. There's a knot in my stomach that twists a little tighter every night. It's important the general public sees us as real people. We need to work with the media now before the trial starts because we already know Rob's people are probably going to try and rip us apart on the stand. Our sanity, our motivations, our memories, everything. That's their job. To undermine us. Our dialogue and stories need to be fresh in people's minds. Please, I ask her, please talk to Time's Up, because we don't have money for PR. And the way they're helping other survivors, I mean, why aren't they helping us?

To my relief, Louise calls the organization on our behalf, leading to a conference call with all of us on it. Everyone on the other side is so quiet. It's uncomfortable, cold, not what I expected from what I'd heard about them. They want to know what we expect them to do, but we already sent paperwork back and forth about this. There was already a plan in the works, waiting for approval. What do they mean what are we expecting? Caught off guard, Lisa Van Allen and I start to talk about Lifetime and Robert and the labels and how someone needs to take responsibility for what's been going on for twenty-something years. We need help. That's what we need. We don't have the resources or the skills to approach this on our own.

Their response?

It didn't happen in the workplace.

What do you mean *it didn't happen in the workplace*?! R. Kelly did this in the studios! Working. Recording. Writing music. Taking female artists under his wing. At his workplace that had owners and bosses and staff. Some of us thought we were working on our careers, too! We thought it was a job opportunity. When we weren't working, we were being raped, hurt, controlled, but it was still at the workplace.

They decide not to help us with any kind of funding. I end up referred to some bullshit lawyers and it's left at that. I already have a lawyer. There are PR firm connections here to help survivors and, what, none of them want to take us on as clients? No one thinks we should be funded to get this kind of help? Once again, I'm left hanging. All the ladies hurt by R. Kelly are left hanging.

I did press for the docuseries because I thought I was helping, pushing towards justice. I don't care for interviews. They're stressful and make you into more of a target, but I want to be an advocate for women—and, now, for me. I don't want more desperate souls out there sharing my past experiences if there's any way to avoid it. I feel like there's a reason I went through all this (and am still going through it). But to be that onscreen advocate, you must be ready for the public, presentable, etc. You can't go on television looking all crazy, feeling destroyed still. No one offered to help me with that. Instead, it feels like I've been rooting for myself all alone.

I didn't just ask Lifetime for random money, I asked for a job or compensation for how much I was putting forward. I asked for therapy after the docuseries experience broke me. It looks like it's always all about the bottom dollar when they're dealing with us. Somehow, we never seem to be seen as equals, regardless of everyone blasting the women-of-color "support" everywhere. Empty words.

Tamra Simmons' branding company has a motto referring to their work as being "dream engineers." For someone who works so hard with public strategy and image assessment and perception… why are all the survivors on this project being targeted and gaslit? Seems like she knows enough about that stuff to influence media and such in our favor.

It's painful, really, to watch other women in similar positions be interviewed, brought on Oprah, supported by both media and advocacy organizations seeking to publicly help them out. Of course I want them to be taken care of; that's not the issue. It's that we need it too. We've needed it all along, since we were kids. Why isn't anyone saying, "Get these girls some help!" Celebrities, companies, wealthy elites, tech gurus… they've all donated to these movements to help women like us. Often that support doesn't quite make it to us. Bottom line: at the end of the day, nobody gives a shit. Someone should have cared.

We're not standard, beautiful actresses; we're regular women of color. Maybe we don't fit the mold or we're a little bit rough around the edges. But what's *wrong* with us that we don't deserve real assistance? Are we the wrong color? The wrong gender? Both? We don't clean up nice enough for them? We're ghetto? Maybe people just want to be part of the suffering experience, the emotional aspect, the guilt. Not participate in slowly shifting us out of the dark, onto a more solid road and better lives. It's the less dramatic side, helping us actually succeed.

This is the situation we've been up against the entire time—way before Lifetime wanted to shoot a docuseries. It was an issue back when no one cared before about the little underage girl in the R. Kelly home video and just let it go. When the record labels knew and didn't do anything. When execs knew and didn't do anything. When no one protected us before or now. No one wants to help *us* unless it's seen as an extreme movement of their incredible graciousness and forward-thinking. That is not *for* us.

As a result, we have been mishandled by the media and the networks. They've exploited our stories and left us broken without support or safety.

Hollywood needs reform for dealing with survivors. Reform isn't about putting on a show. Reform happens in the little things, sometimes in what you don't see behind the scenes. And if no one is willing to take us on publicly in an extreme show of backing us, then absolutely no one is going to covertly put a bunch of effort in. I'm not afraid anymore. This is the story. Mistreated. Mishandled. Taken advantage of. It's like being raped all over again.

***

The countless women who loved Rob, stayed with him, isolated themselves in hotel rooms, waited for him outside of trials… we're not crazy. No one is all bad, as easy as it is to slap that on a person. Rob's a mysterious musical genius who's bad, beautiful, mean, nice, and ugly all wrapped up into one. There's a sweet side anyone would fall in love with, and it comes through sometimes in his music, which is why his stuff attracts such intensity in his fans.

Robert was abused as a child, some part of him never grew up, giving him both an ugly and an endearingly sweet side. Anyone could fall in love with the charming musician who needed love. I wanted to understand him, and, deep down, I wanted to save him. I couldn't, and no one can, but I wanted to. I tried to leave, several times, telling myself I could do more with my life, but my situation always came back to him. He could get me further when I felt lost, when I had nothing left and nowhere to go. His "tactics" aren't to drive people away. He wants you to stay, girl, because he wants devotion in return. He hurts so much, even *I* saw him as the victim for years, and in some ways, he is.

What kind of thing happens in your life to be like that? To need that much. Nothing normal. That's for damn sure.

Despite the many times my story has been told and there being other women with shared experiences, I still always get the same question: Why did you stay?

Why do you think I stayed? I wasn't hiding out in hotels, pressing my face to the floor of the car for fame or my music career. I loved him. And before I truly loved him, he offered hope. I met Robert when I was an underage teenager, still essentially a child, abused by three people already and wanting to trust someone but unaware how the world worked. When you're in that position, no one can really tell you. Neglected by my mom, I adjusted to accept strange or hurtful behavior to deal with the people in my early life. None of this made me think I would end up here. This isn't something you pick, but I can assure you, those people pick you. That goes for relationships, friendships, bosses, etc.

By the time Rob was asking me to do what he wanted, I'd been abused by a family member, my mom's ex-boyfriend, and the father of a girl I babysat. Both abused and neglected, I had been trained to accept the abuse of older, more mature adults... and excuse them for it. I was an easy target for a man over ten years older than me. I was also an easy target for the media years later. Doing what I'm told, accepting abuse, not standing up for myself, because no one has time for it. No one was waiting for me to get it together just so I could figure it out and strike back. There is no justice for me by law because it's too late. I never want it to be too late for someone else in this kind of pain.

So the mutually abused side, yeah, it hurts me, but it also makes me more empathetic. Do not blame me for feeling for Rob when he told me his stories. I would be heartless not to, and as you can see, there are plenty of heartless people in the world at all levels anyway, with only their own success in mind.

Lifetime, and the other companies involved, they didn't treat us well. And it's not a secret. Their editors knew it was happening even just in relation to the storyline direction. This isn't nitpicking, I'm talking about how the series was presenting Rob's importance over us. Those editors left.

They knew what that line of directing would lead to, and what it meant.

For the survivors, all our trauma is back fresh in our heads, and I'm just hoping to God that writing mine down will be cathartic and tell the whole story, not just the one the media and directors cut and pasted together for drama. Not just the one that makes other people cry and then move on with their lives five minutes later.

The media and the networks? They can be just as bad as the men. Use us and discard us. These companies knew I had no clue, that I was all heart, and they took advantage of that. They should be ashamed of themselves and exposed for what they truly are to many women out there. Predators.

They used our likeness and our pain and sold it and resold it all over the world. And here I am, living in a month-to-month place where I don't even know how I'm gonna pay rent next month. No one wants to help with the normal, the everyday. People want to be seen as saviors, benefactors. They want to watch our pain and go through the catharsis with us and then sit on the other side feeling good about having any feelings at all. Good thing they purged all that negativity from the world by feeling bad for an hour on a Thursday night.

What we trauma survivors need is to be able to live well from day to day. When one of the producers, during a magazine interview, made a comment about how so many people were being healed from this project, I wanted to ask who. The executives' pocketbooks? The public with the guilty conscience? The corporations and record labels who have ignored us for years and now watch *Surviving R. Kelly*? I mean, it's not us. Not the women on the actual episodes, that's for sure. We became victims all over again with new kinds of predators to watch out for.

The repercussions of standing up and opening up about the truth may continue to distort my future career and health. I might keep losing everything again and again while I seek justice and stand with the other survivors. I might never get back the life I had managed to build before.

You can see me on Netflix, though. You can see me on Netflix every damn night of the week.

Epilogue

On September 27th, 2021, the jury of the federal court in Brooklyn, New York, found Robert Sylvester Kelly guilty on all counts. These charges included one count of racketeering—this involved fourteen individual acts based on sexual exploitation of children, recruiting underage women, bribery, forced labor, and kidnapping—and eight violations of the Mann Act. Kelly's sentencing is set for May 2022, where he may face life in prison. He also faces charges in Chicago, Illinois and the state of Minnesota.

***

When the news hit, it was hard to get air. Robert was found guilty on all counts in his New York trial. Nothing can describe the absolute relief of seeing those words in bold print. I ended up not having to testify in court. I was ready, but I also know it would have been traumatizing to look into his face again and speak against him. Behind the relief and the sense of victory from justice finally working its way around, I am so exhausted I can hardly stay up. My entire being is emotionally drained from years of waiting for this man to be held accountable, plus everything I went through with him before that. I don't feel bad for him. I can't anymore. He did this to himself, and I'm finally free. I know this can't happen to anyone else.

Today, I start to unpack this whole ordeal. I need to move on and move forward. I need to be set free from within. I'm focusing on myself one hour at a time. It's all you can do.

To my readers.

I want to thank you for reading my story. Never in a million years would I have ever thought I would publish a book. I want you all to know that if any of you have suffered abuse in your lives, I stand with you. You are worth it. If any of you are now living in an abusive situation, look at yourself in the mirror and tell yourself, "I am worth it." You are. If I could walk away, so can you. Walk away. It's not going to be easy; however, there is a life after abuse. You are not alone. You are strength and love.

To the young women out there who find themselves in similar situations.

Keep going no matter what. A lot of us don't get the opportunity to come from the best homes, and it's hard to see a way out, or you feel at some point like you have to do certain things to get out. You don't. I don't. I didn't. And I know that now.

I didn't need that guy. That man was the disgrace of my life.

You have the world at your feet. And I pray these words give you hope.

Parents need to wake up too. My parents should have been more woke. They weren't. They were too lost in their own shit to help me with mine. Look out for each other.

The media may have taken my power, but I'm tougher for it. My goal is to help create safe homes for women, particularly one in Miami. In the next couple years, it's going to happen. I didn't have a place to go when I left an abusive husband with my children and nothing else. Women need a safe place, a refuge, for fresh starts. Not to stay there forever, but to become more independent and loved while you're doing it so you can go back into society strong.

Every woman deserves to heal and go back into society strong.

Love always,
Lizzette

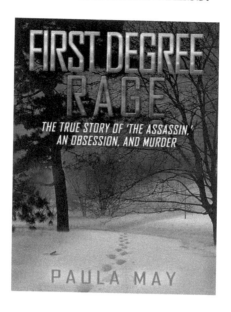

AVAILABLE FROM MONIQUE FAISON ROSS AND WILDBLUE PRESS!

PLAYING DEAD by MONIQUE FAISON ROSS

http://wbp.bz/playingdeada

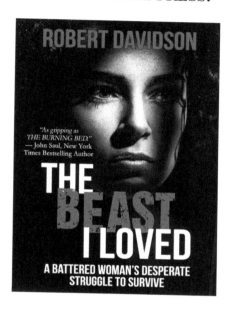

Lightning Source UK Ltd.
Milton Keynes UK
UKHW022016020822
406743UK00005B/564